Maths

The 11+ Practice Book

with Assessment Tests

Ages
10-11

Practise • Prepare • Pass

Everything your child needs for 11+ success

How to use this Practice Book

This book is divided into two parts — themed question practice and full-length assessment tests. There are answers and detailed explanations in the pull-out section at the back of the book.

Themed question practice

- Each page contains practice questions divided by topic. Use these pages to work out your child's strengths and the areas they find tricky. The questions get harder down each page.

Assessment tests

- The second half of the book contains four full-length assessment tests, each with a mix of question types from the first half of the book. They take a similar form to the real test.

- You can print off multiple-choice answer sheets from our website, www.cgplearning.co.uk/11+, so your child can practise taking the tests as if they're sitting the real thing.

- If you want to give your child timed practice, give them a time limit of 50 minutes for each test, and ask them to work as quickly and carefully as they can.

- Your child should aim for a mark of around 85% (43 questions correct) in each test. If they score less than this, use their results to work out the areas they need more practice on.

- If they haven't managed to finish the test in time, they need to work on increasing their speed, whereas if they have made a lot of mistakes, they need to work more carefully.

- Keep track of your child's scores using the progress chart on the inside back cover of the book.

Published by CGP

Editors:
Luke Antieul, David Broadbent, Sharon Keeley-Holden, Sarah Williams

Contributors:
Stephanie Burton, Susan Foord, Julie Hunt, Katrina Saville

With thanks to Joe Brazier and Rachel Murray for the proofreading.

ISBN: 978 1 84762 828 2
Groovy website: www.cgpbooks.co.uk
Printed by Elanders Ltd, Newcastle upon Tyne
Clipart from CorelDRAW®

Based on the classic CGP style created by Richard Parsons.

Photocopying — it's dull, it takes ages… and sometimes it's a bit naughty. Luckily, it's dead cheap, easy and quick to order more copies of this book from CGP — just call us on 0870 750 1242. Phew!

CONTENTS

Place Value

For each row of numbers below, circle the number that has the smallest value.

1. 2076   2109   10 102   1979   2000

2. 1.06   6.15   15.06   10.56   100.50

3. 475.5   54.75   7.55   7.09   15.01

4. 980.1   974.8   98.01   98.45   98.1

5. 0.946   0.878   1.811   1.02   0.923

Copy out the numbers below, and add a decimal point so that each number has 5 tens.

Example: 35982   Answer: _____359.82_____

6. 62520   Answer: _____

7. 51303   Answer: _____

8. 7541   Answer: _____

9. 210522   Answer: _____

10. 325781   Answer: _____

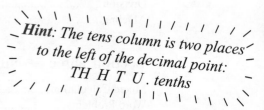

Hint: The tens column is two places to the left of the decimal point:
TH H T U . tenths

/ 5

Write down the number each arrow is pointing to.

11.
35   85   Answer: _____

12.
40   60   Answer: _____

13.
5.8   5.9   Answer: _____

14. Stacey wrote down the heights, in feet (ft), of five mountains in Europe.
    Circle which one is the tallest.

    11 227 ft   11 293 ft   10 991 ft   11 112 ft   11 242 ft

15. Which of these pairs of   14.61 and 13.49
    numbers are the same   14.4 and 13.8
    distance from 14?   13.33 and 14.33
                                     13.82 and 14.18
                                     13.74 and 14.36   Answer: _____

/ 5

Rounding Up and Down

Circle each correctly rounded answer.

1.	6726 to the nearest 100	6720	6800	6700	7000	6730
2.	9345 to the nearest 10	9340	9346	9350	9400	9300
3.	64.77 to the nearest whole number	65	65.70	60	64	64.7
4.	0.287 to the nearest hundredth	0.29	0.30	0.20	0.289	0.299
5.	1095.93 to the nearest 100	1096	1100	1090	1105	1000

/ 5

Round 4990.63 to:

6. the nearest 10.   Answer: _____

7. the nearest 1000.   Answer: _____

8. the nearest tenth.   Answer: _____

9. the nearest whole number.   Answer: _____

10. the nearest 100.   Answer: _____

/ 5

11. Which of these is equal to 2400?
   A   2351 rounded to the nearest 1000
   B   2347 rounded to the nearest 100
   C   2356 rounded to the nearest 10
   D   2389 rounded to the nearest 10
   E   2439 rounded to the nearest 100   Answer: _____

12. A number rounded to the nearest 10 is 37 040.
    What is the smallest number this could be?   Answer: _____

13. Round 437 985 to the nearest 10 000.   Answer: _____

14. Round 36.572 kg to the nearest 100 g.   Answer: _____ kg

15. Round 175.639 m to the nearest 10 cm.   Answer: _____ m

/ 5

Section One — Number Knowledge

Number Knowledge

Circle 'True' or 'False' for each statement in questions 1-3.

1. An even number plus an odd number is always an even number.   True / False

2. An odd number times an even number is always an odd number.   True / False

3. Multiples of 3 are always odd.   True / False

4. Circle the number which has the smallest value.

     -3   -1.5   0   0.2   2.1

5. Circle the highest temperature.

     -27 °C   -15 °C   -1 °C   -8 °C   -2 °C

 / 5

Complete each calculation using a <, > or = sign.
Use the number line to help you.

Hint: Remember, < means 'less than', and > means 'greater than'.

6. -8 _____ 5

7. -4 + 2 _____ 2

8. -3 + 7 _____ 4

-8 -7 -6 -5 -4 -3 -2 -1 0 1 2 3 4 5 6 7 8

9. -2 + 6 _____ 7 – 5

10. -7 + 1 _____ 5 – 13

 / 5

11. What is the sum of the even numbers between 1 and 11?   Answer: _____

12. What is the sum of the odd numbers between 20 and 26?   Answer: _____

13. Circle the number which is a factor of both 20 and 32.

     16   4   10   8   5

14. Circle the set of numbers which contains only multiples of 3 or 4.

     3, 10, 12   4, 8, 10   15, 18, 22   12, 15, 16   20, 25, 30

15. Circle the number which is exactly divisible by both 6 and 9.

     12   18   27   30   45

16. The temperature in five cities is shown in the table.
What is the difference between the highest and the lowest temperatures?

Answer: _____ °C

City	Temperature
Cairo	12°C
Frankfurt	0°C
Helsinki	-13°C
London	2°C
Paris	-1°C

/ 6

Number Knowledge

17. Anna is holding a party for six children. She buys cupcakes which come in boxes of four. The children eat all the cupcakes and they all get the same number. What is the fewest number of boxes that Anna could have bought?

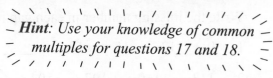

Answer: _____

18. Emma is planting rows of seeds. In the first row, she places beetroot seeds 9 cm apart. In the second row, she places lettuce seeds 15 cm apart. The first seeds in the two rows are in line. After what distance will a beetroot seed be in line with a lettuce seed again?

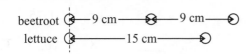

Answer: _____ cm

19. How many whole numbers under 10 will go in the shaded area on the Venn diagram?

Answer: _____

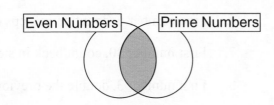

20. Which statement is correct?

 A $7 \times 120 < 20 \times 35$
 B $8 \times 110 = 20 \times 35$
 C $6 \times 130 > 20 \times 35$
 D $7 \times 100 < 20 \times 35$
 E $6 \times 110 > 20 \times 35$

Answer: _____

21. What is the lowest positive whole number that will go into the 'Not Prime' and 'Not Square' section of the sorting diagram?

Answer: _____

	Square	Not Square
Prime		
Not Prime		

22. Feroz's age is a square number. His younger brother's age is also a square number. The sum of their ages is 20 years. How old is Feroz?

Answer: _____

23. What is the smallest square number which has both 2 and 5 as factors?

Answer: _____

24. Which number has been placed in the wrong section of the Venn diagram?

Answer: _____

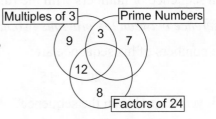

25. Brian is thinking of a number. The number is the sum of 4 square numbers which are also factors of 64. What is the number?

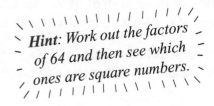

Answer: _____

/ 9

Section One — Number Knowledge

Number Sequences

Write the missing number in each gap in the sequences below.

1. 9   12   15   18   ____

2. 113   110   107   104   ____

3. 26   21   ____   11   6

4. 1.25   1.5   1.75   ____   2.25

5. ____   8   16   32   64

/ 5

Write down the fifth number in the sequence which follows each rule below.

6. First number 6, count on in steps of 4.   Answer: _____

7. First number 30, count back in steps of 5.   Answer: _____

8. First number 3, double the previous number.   Answer: _____

9. First number 19, count back in steps of 4.   Answer: _____

10. First number 5, count on in steps of $\frac{1}{2}$.   Answer: _____

/ 5

For questions 11 and 12, write down how many sticks are needed to make the next shape in the sequence.

11.

Answer: _____

12.

Answer: _____

13. John writes a sequence of numbers with the rule:

    Find the difference between the previous two numbers.

    The first five numbers of his sequence are:

    20   25   5   20   15

    What is the seventh number in the sequence?   Answer: _____

14. Tom counts back from 73 in steps of 9. Mark counts forward from 25 in steps of 4. What number will both boys count?   Answer: _____

15. Nadiah counts back from 6 in steps of 1.25. What is the first negative number she will count?

    Answer: _____

/ 5

Section One — Number Knowledge

Fractions

Find:

1. ½ of 12   Answer: _____

2. ⅓ of 9   Answer: _____

3. ⅔ of 8   Answer: _____

4. ⅖ of 24   Answer: _____

5. ¾ of 36   Answer: _____

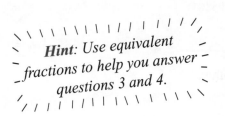

Hint: Use equivalent fractions to help you answer questions 3 and 4.

/ 5

Circle the largest amount in each pair given below.

6. ¼ of 32   ⅓ of 27

7. ⅔ of 33   ⅕ of 100

8. ⅖ of 25   ½ of 18

9. ⅘ of 35   ⅚ of 30

10. ⅓ of 120   ⅞ of 48

/ 5

11. Mrs Osborne has 8 apples to share equally between 12 children. What fraction of a whole apple should she give to each child? Circle the correct answer.

    ⁷⁄₉   ⅔   ¾   ⁶⁄₇   ⅗

12. What fraction of this shape is shaded?
    Circle the correct answer.

    ⅜   ⅓   ¾   ½   ⅗

13. How many sixths are there in 5 ½?

    Answer: _____

14. Martha has some marbles. She gives ⅖ of them to Joseph.
    Martha now has 12 marbles left.
    How many marbles did Martha have to start with?   Answer: _____

15. Aarti wants to buy 4 dog chews.
    What is the difference in the price of
    4 dog chews from these two shops?

Dog Empire
Dog chews. £1 each. Buy one get one half price!

Dog Shop
Dog chews. £1.20 each. Buy 3 or more and save ⅓ on the total price!

    Answer: _____ p

/ 5

Section One — Number Knowledge

Percentages, Fractions and Decimals

Fill in each missing percentage, fraction or decimal below.

1. 29%   =   _____   =   0.29

2. 15%   =   ³⁄₂₀   =   _____

3. _____%   =   ³¹⁄₅₀   =   0.62

4. 46%   =   _____   =   0.46

5. 3%   =   ³⁄₁₀₀   =   _____

/ 5

Find the following amounts.

6. 10% of 70   Answer: _____

7. 25% of 12   Answer: _____

8. 75% of 48   Answer: _____

9. 2% of 6400   Answer: _____

10. 30% of 80   Answer: _____

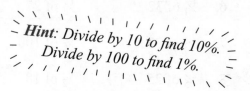

Hint: Divide by 10 to find 10%.
Divide by 100 to find 1%.

/ 5

11. What percentage of this shape is not shaded?

    Answer: _____ %

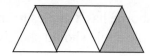

12. The price of a football has been reduced by 20% in a sale.
    Before the sale it cost £10.50.
    What is the reduced price of the football?   Answer: £ _____

13. Mr Parkinson has 30 rose bushes in his garden.
    40% of them have red flowers, ¹⁄₆ of them have
    yellow flowers, and the rest have white flowers.
    How many of Mr Parkinson's rose bushes
    have white flowers?   Answer: _____

14. The table shows how pupils in Class 6B at
    Park Rise School get to school each day.
    What percentage of the pupils travel by bus?

    Answer: _____ %

Type of Transport	Number of Pupils
Walk	10
Bicycle	4
Bus	12
Car	4

15. Circle the calculation which gives the largest answer.

    25% of 88   ²⁄₃ of 36   ⁴⁄₅ of 30   20% of 80   75% of 40

/ 5

Section One — Number Knowledge

Addition

Write down the answer to each calculation.

1. 72 + 56   Answer: _____

2. 135 + 258   Answer: _____

3. 268 + 945   Answer: _____

4. 1076 + 1177   Answer: _____

5. 3303 + 4868   Answer: _____

/ 5

Write down the answer to each calculation.

6. 6.2 + 17.8   Answer: _____

7. 9.3 + 3.5   Answer: _____

8. 11.23 + 4.58   Answer: _____

9. 25.7 + 24.5   Answer: _____

10. 34.23 + 22.73   Answer: _____

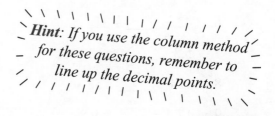

Hint: If you use the column method for these questions, remember to line up the decimal points.

/ 5

11. Jasmine and Tom went to the sweet shop. Jasmine bought a
    chocolate bar for 38p and a carton of orange juice for 64p.
    Tom bought a banana for 32p and bubblegum for 29p.
    How much did they spend in total?   Answer: £ _____

12. Daha planted a sunflower seed. After 4 weeks it had grown
    to be 4 cm tall. It then grew 2 cm in week 5, 3.5 cm in
    week 6, 4.4 cm in week 7 and 4.7 cm in week 8.
    How tall was Daha's sunflower after 8 weeks?   Answer: _____ cm

13. Julie bought a washing machine for £490.90, a
    vacuum cleaner for £55.50 and a coffee machine
    for £127.20. How much did she spend in total?   Answer: £ _____

14. Mr Brown stops for a snack at the Quick Café and spends
    exactly £3.55. Which items did he buy? Circle the answer.

    A   Bacon roll, full breakfast
    B   Full breakfast, toast and jam, tea
    C   Full breakfast, coffee
    D   Bacon roll, toast and jam, coffee
    E   Full breakfast, tea

Quick Café Menu	
Bacon roll	£1.45
Toast and jam	£1.25
Full breakfast	£1.85
Tea	75p
Coffee	85p

15. Farrah posts four parcels weighing 24.5 kg, 16.2 kg,
    6.25 kg and 5.4 kg. What is the total weight of these parcels?

/ 5

    Answer: _____ kg

Subtraction

Write down the answer to each calculation.

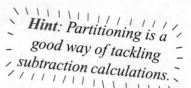

Hint: Partitioning is a good way of tackling subtraction calculations.

1. 56 – 32   Answer: _____

2. 84 – 29   Answer: _____

3. 1062 – 358   Answer: _____

4. 264.3 – 82.5   Answer: _____

5. 13.2 – 4.16   Answer: _____

/ 5

Fill in the missing number in each of the following calculations:

6. 42 – _____ = 31

7. 5.3 – _____ = 2.1

8. 124 – _____ = 52

9. 17.4 – _____ = 9.8

10. 664 – _____ = 406

/ 5

11. Shefali baked 48 cakes. She decorated 12 with chocolate icing, 15 with lemon, 6 with orange, 9 with strawberry and the rest with coffee icing. How many cakes were decorated with coffee icing?

    Answer: _____

12. 60 children went on a school trip. The coach dropped them off at different places on the way home. Patrick recorded the number of children who got off at each point. Church Avenue was the last stop, so everyone left on the bus got off. How many children got off at Church Avenue?

    Answer: _____

Bus Stop	Number who got off the bus
Creek Street	15
Exeter Street	7
New Street	4
Crompton Road	9
Market Square	14
Church Avenue	

13. Mr Reid has a plank of wood which is 320 cm long. On Monday he cut off 120 cm of wood from the plank. On Tuesday he cut off 63 cm. On Wednesday he cut off another 66 cm. How long was the remaining plank of wood?

    Answer: _____ cm

14. Rona and Jenny went to the newsagents. Rona spent £2.60 on a comic and £1.22 on a birthday card. Jenny bought a magazine for £3.20 and a bottle of water for 75p. How much more did Jenny spend than Rona?

    Answer: _____ p

15. Jonathan had £42. He spent £26.99 on a model car, £6.99 on a joke book and £2.46 on a giant bar of chocolate. How much money did he have left?

    Answer: _____

/ 5

Multiplying and Dividing by 10, 100 and 1000

Write down the answer to each calculation.

1. 12×100 Answer: _____

2. 3.6×1000 Answer: _____

3. 0.24×10 Answer: _____

4. 169.454×100 Answer: _____

5. 0.062×1000 Answer: _____   / 5

Write down the answer to each calculation.

6. $3472 \div 100$ Answer: _____

7. $94.6 \div 10$ Answer: _____

8. $48.3 \div 100$ Answer: _____

9. $0.46 \div 10$ Answer: _____

10. $3205 \div 1000$ Answer: _____   / 5

11. $4720 = 100 \times$ ____
    What is the missing number? Circle the correct answer.
    A 472   **B** 47.2   **C** 47   **D** 47 200   **E** 47 200

12. Martin is making a scale model of his school.
    He measures the length of the actual science block as 2224 cm.
    He wants his model to be 100 times smaller than the real building.
    How long should his model science block be?   Answer: _____ cm

13. A pack of 10 pens costs £2.70.
    A box of pens contains 100 packs.
    Mrs Chapman buys 10 boxes of pens.
    How much does this cost?   Answer: £ _____

14. Kailash thinks of a number. He multiplies it by 100, then divides
    the answer by 10. Finally he multiplies the result by 1000.
    What single calculation could he have done to get to this answer?   Answer: _____

15. The population of Ampney is 10 times larger than the population of Bentley.
    The population of Bentley is 1000 times smaller than the population of Clifton.
    The population of Clifton is 10 times larger than the population of Dannett.
    If the population of Ampney is 2630, what is the population of Dannett?   / 5

    Answer: _____

Multiplication

Write down the answer to each calculation.

1. 13×8 Answer: _____

2. 9×24 Answer: _____

3. 17×14 Answer: _____

4. 330×5 Answer: _____

5. 65×22 Answer: _____

/ 5

Write down the answer to each calculation.

6. 3.6×6 Answer: _____

7. 4.2×7 Answer: _____

8. 9.3×8 Answer: _____

9. 6.4×70 Answer: _____

10. 0.23×5 Answer: _____

/ 5

11. How much would it cost for 4 children to go swimming?

    Answer: £ _____

	Swimming Prices
Adult	£2.30
Child	£1.95

12. How much will 7 bags of bird seed cost if 2 bags cost 24p?   Answer: _____ p

13. The table shows the ingredients needed to make 8 pancakes.
    How many grams of flour are needed to make 40 pancakes?

    Answer: _____ g

Pancake Ingredients
110 g flour
270 ml milk
Pinch of salt
1 egg

14.
$$3.24 \times 52 = 168.48$$

    What is 32.4×5.2?   Answer: _____

15. What is 7.7×6.4?

    A   62.74
    B   38.56
    C   0.532
    D   49.28
    E   4.86   Answer: _____

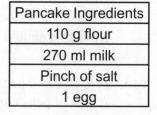

Hint: Use rounding to estimate the answer.

16.
$$268 \times 94 = 25\ 192$$

    What is 268×188?   Answer: _____

/ 6

Section Two — Working with Numbers

Multiplication

17. Which calculation has the largest value?

    A 52.7×0.8
    B 0.527×80
    C 5.27×800
    D 527×0.8
    E 5270×0.008 Answer: _____

18. $241 \times 32 = 7712$
    Which of the answers below is incorrect?

    Hint: Halving one number in a multiplication means the product is halved too.

    A $241 \times 8 = 7712 \div 4$
    B $241 \times 64 = 7712 \times 2$
    C $241 \times 16 = 7712 \div 2$
    D $241 \times 33 = 7953$
    E $241 \times 4 = 7712 \div 16$ Answer: _____

19. Betty, Dave and Lorna collect stickers. Betty has
    26 stickers in her collection. Dave has 7 times as many
    stickers as Betty. Lorna has 3 times as many as Betty.
    How many stickers do the three children have all together?   Answer: _____

20. Which calculation has the largest value?

    A 6×4000
    B 70×300
    C 200×200
    D 900×10
    E 8×500 Answer: _____

21. Which calculation has the smallest value?

    A 4.82×0.06
    B 2.41×0.06
    C 2.41×0.12
    D 4.82×0.12
    E 9.64×0.06 Answer: _____

22. If the answers to the following calculations were put in size
    order from smallest to largest, which would be in the middle?

    A 47×256
    B 4.7×2.56
    C 0.47×2.56
    D 47×25.6
    E 4.7×25.6 Answer: _____

23. 40 bags of grain weighing 12.5 kg each have a
    total weight of 500 kg. What would the total
    weight be of 80 bags weighing 25 kg each?

    / 7

    Answer: _____ kg

Division

Write down the answer to each calculation.

1. $96 \div 6$ Answer: _____

2. $124 \div 4$ Answer: _____

3. $720 \div 5$ Answer: _____

4. $856 \div 8$ Answer: _____

5. $67.2 \div 3$ Answer: _____

/ 5

Write down the remainder in each calculation.

6. $37 \div 5$ Answer: _____

7. $103 \div 4$ Answer: _____

8. $126 \div 8$ Answer: _____

9. $186 \div 9$ Answer: _____

10. $244 \div 8$ Answer: _____

/ 5

11. Year 6 are going on a trip. There are 81
    children and 10 members of staff. How many
    7-seater minibuses do they need to hire?   Answer: _____

12. Sunita has a 560 cm length of ribbon. She cuts it into 8
    equal pieces. How long, in centimetres, is each piece?   Answer: _____ cm

13. Claire has 139 pencil sharpeners. She packs them
    into boxes of 8. How many boxes will she need?   Answer: _____

14. Mr Bond is setting out chairs for the school assembly.
    He can fit 9 chairs in each row. How many complete
    rows will he be able to make with 300 chairs?   Answer: _____

15. Mrs Revitt has 128 photos to put up on the display board in rows.
    She wants there to be the same number of photos in each row.
    How many photos should she put in each row to
    make sure she has no photos left over?

    A   3
    B   4
    C   5
    D   6
    E   7   Answer: _____

/ 5

Algebra

If $a = 6$, work out the value of the following expressions.

1. $a + 5$ Answer: _____

2. $4a$ Answer: _____

3. $2a - 3$ Answer: _____

4. $3a + 2a$ Answer: _____

5. $5(a + 4)$ Answer: _____

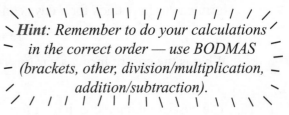

Hint: Remember to do your calculations in the correct order — use BODMAS (brackets, other, division/multiplication, addition/subtraction).

/ 5

Circle the answer in each row which is equal to the first expression.

6. $a + a$ $2(a + 1)$ $2a$ a^2

7. $3 \times n - 2$ $3n - 2$ $3n - 6$ $3n - 32$

8. $5x + 2x$ $x + 7$ $4x + 3x$ $5(x + 2)$

9. $3(2a + b)$ $6a + 6b$ $6a + 3b$ $32a + 3b$

10. $2m - 2m$ $2m - 1$ $-2m$ $2m - 2(m + 0)$

/ 5

11. $4 \times 7 > 3x$

What is the biggest number that x could represent?

A   7
B   8
C   9
D   10
E   11   Answer: _____

12. The time, in minutes, required to bake a cake is given by the formula $60 + 5e$. The letter e is the number of eggs used in the recipe. How many minutes would it take to bake a cake made with 8 eggs?

A   70
B   80
C   90
D   100
E   110   Answer: _____

13. Mr Carpenter has a 400 cm long plank of wood. He cuts off three pieces which are each x cm long. Which expression gives the length of wood he has left in cm?

A $400 \div 3x$
B $400 - x$
C $400 - 3x$
D $400 \times 3x$
E $400 + 3x$ Answer: _____

/ 3

Section Two — Working with Numbers

Algebra

14. Hiring a car costs £75 plus £50 for each day it is hired. The total cost of hiring a car in pounds for d days can be calculated using the expression:

$$75 + 50d$$

What is the cost of hiring a car for 9 days?   Answer: £_____

15. The cost of taking a coach on a ferry is £260 for the vehicle and driver, and a further £5 for each passenger. Which expression could you use to show the cost, in pounds, of taking a coach and p passengers on the ferry?

    A $260 - 5p$
    B $260p - 5$
    C $260 \times p$
    D $260 \div 5p$
    E $260 + 5p$ Answer: _____

16. Mr Lee buys a games console for £150, and some games to play on it for £35 each. If he buys n games, which expression represents the total amount he spent?

    A $150 + 35n$
    B $150n \times 35$
    C $150 - 35n$
    D $150 \times 35n$
    E $150 \times 35 \div n$ Answer: _____

17. Peter makes up a rule for the nth term of a sequence. He uses it to generate the sequence:

$$3, \quad 7, \quad 11, \quad 15, \quad 19...$$

Circle the rule below that Peter used.

   $n + 4$ $3n + 4$ $4n + 3$ $4n - 1$ $n + 2$

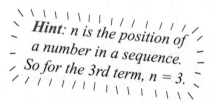

Hint: n is the position of a number in a sequence. So for the 3rd term, n = 3.

18. Paul is doing a sponsored silence. Paul works out that if he is silent for m minutes the amount of pounds raised will be:

$$15 + 2(m + 2)$$

How many pounds will Paul raise if he is silent for 25 minutes?   Answer: £ _____

19. Fatima lays her marbles out in a series of patterns. There are $\frac{1}{2} n(n + 1)$ marbles in the nth pattern. How many marbles will be in the 8th pattern?

Pattern 1   Pattern 2   Pattern 3   Pattern 4

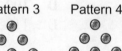

20. George is selling advertising space in a magazine. A full page advert costs £F, and a half page advert is half the price. If George sells 5 full page and 8 half page adverts, circle the formula which represents the amount he will earn.

   $\frac{1}{2} \times 5F + 8F$ $5F + \frac{1}{2} \times 8F$ $F(5 + 8)$ $2F + \frac{1}{2} \times 8$ $F + \frac{1}{2}(5 \times 8)$

/ 7

Mixed Calculations

Write down the answer to each calculation.

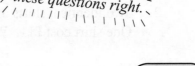
Hint: You need to use BODMAS to get these questions right.

1. $7 + 4 \times 6 - 3$ Answer: _____

2. $6 + 8 \div 2 - 1$ Answer: _____

3. $7 + 6 - 5 \times 2$ Answer: _____

4. $9 \times 5 + 6 \times 3$ Answer: _____

5. $3 \times 5 + 15 \div 5$ Answer: _____

/ 5

Complete each calculation using a +, −, × or ÷ sign.

6. $7 \underline{} (6 + 4) = 70$

7. $9 \underline{} (3 \times 2) = 3$

8. $3 \underline{} (8 \times 1) = 11$

9. $27 \underline{} (11 - 2) = 3$

10. $(4 \underline{} 5) + 1 = 21$

/ 5

11. What is $89 \times 296 + 11 \times 296$?
     Circle the correct answer.

     42 560   2344   29 600   39 200   58 080

12. Which calculation has the largest value?
        A $7 + 6 - 4 \times 3$
        B $7 \times 6 - 4 + 3$
        C $7 - 6 + 4 \times 3$
        D $7 \times 6 + 4 - 3$
        E $7 + 6 \times 4 - 3$ Answer: _____

13. Mike wants to work out how much it will cost for his family
     to go to the cinema. They need tickets for 2 adults, 1 student,
     3 children and 2 seniors. Circle the option below which will
     complete this calculation to find the total cost of the tickets:

     $3 \times £3 + 3 \times £4 + 2 \times £5$ _____

     + 40p   − 40p   − 60 p   + 50p   + 60p

Ticket Prices	
Adult	£4.95
Child	£2.95
Student	£3.95
Senior	£3.95

14. Which calculation has the smallest value?
        A $60 - 20 + 10 \div 5$
        B $60 - 20 \div 10 + 5$
        C $60 + 20 - 10 \div 5$
        D $60 + 20 \div 10 - 5$
        E $60 \div 20 + 10 - 5$ Answer: _____

15. What is $420 \div (60 \times 3.5)$?

     Answer: _____

/ 5

Word Problems

1. Matt worked for 3 hours on Monday, 4 hours on Tuesday
   and 3 hours on Wednesday. He was paid £8 an hour.
   How much money did he receive?   Answer: £ _____

2. Two identical shirts and one tie cost £24.
   One shirt cost £11. What is the cost of the tie?   Answer: £ _____

3. Finlay got a box of 56 chocolates for his birthday.
   He decided to eat eight each day. After how many
   days had he eaten half of the chocolates?   Answer: _____

4. Oscar shares out his sweets equally between his friends. They each end up
   with 9 sweets. Circle the amount of sweets Oscar could have started with.

   84   96   78   67   81

5. It takes exactly 5 litres of paint to mark out 130 parking spaces.
   How many parking spaces can be painted using 3 litres of paint?   Answer: _____

6. Which of the following sets of items would cost exactly £6.25?
   Circle the correct answer.

Stationery Prices	
Calculator	£4.50
Ruler	£1.00
Pencil	25p
Rubber	75p
Sharpener	£1.50

   A   1 calculator, 1 rubber, 2 pencils
   B   4 pencils, 2 sharpeners
   C   1 calculator, 1 ruler, 1 rubber
   D   3 rulers, 3 pencils, 1 rubber
   E   1 calculator, 1 sharpener

7. Mrs Leith has five balls of wool weighing 750 g
   in total. She uses two of them to knit some mittens.
   What weight of wool does she have left?   Answer: _____ g

8. Basil is making fish pie to feed 4 people.
   The recipe is for 6 people, and uses 1.2 kg of fish.
   How many kilograms of fish should Basil buy?   Answer: _____ kg

9. Anusha thinks of a number, squares it, then divides
   the answer by 10. The number she ends up with is 6.4.
   What number did Anusha start with?   Answer: _____

10. Jack's mum bought him 2 football shirts, a
    pair of football boots and 3 pairs of socks.
    How much change did she get from £100?

Football Kit Prices	
Boots	£32
Shirts	£12.50
Shorts	£8.50
Socks	£2.25

    Answer: £ _____

11. A pack of five small candles costs £5.50. A pack of two
    large candles costs three times as much as a pack of five
    small candles. How much does each large candle cost?

    Answer: £ _____

/ 11

Section Three — Number Problems

Word Problems

12. Connor bought six choc ices. He gave the shop assistant £7
    and got 10p in change. How much did each choc ice cost?   Answer: £ _____

13. One jelly snake weighs 2¾ grams and costs 4p. Arthur spends
    24p on jelly snakes. Circle the weight of snakes he bought.

         11 g   66.5 g   36 g   16.5 g   25 g

14. Chris is serving tea and coffee at a concert. In the first hour
    he sells 57 drinks. Circle the statement that cannot be true.

    A   Chris sold more teas than coffees.
    B   Most people bought coffee.
    C   Chris sold five more teas than coffees.
    D   Chris sold twice as many coffees as teas.
    E   Ten more teas than coffees were sold.

15. Mr Churchill builds a brick wall. Each brick has a height of 15 cm.
    He puts a 2 cm thick layer of concrete between each row of bricks.
    He also puts a 2 cm thick concrete layer beneath the first row of bricks.
    The finished wall has 10 rows of bricks. How high is the wall?

    15 cm
    2 cm

    Answer: _____ cm

16. A 2 litre bottle of blackcurrant concentrate makes enough
    squash to fill six 800 ml jugs. How many litres of concentrate
    are needed to fill 48 glasses, each holding 200 ml of squash?   Answer: _____ l

17. Some Year 6 students organised a charity car wash day. They bought enough
    soap and wax to wash exactly 100 cars. It costs them 24p to wash each car.
    How much money would they raise for charity if they wash
    100 cars, and charge £1.20 for each car?   Answer: £ _____

18. Ben wants to make some rock cakes and
    lemon buns. Eggs cost 22p each. How
    much will it cost to buy enough eggs to
    bake 36 rock cakes and 60 lemon buns?

Rock Cakes (makes 24)	
Flour	450 g
Eggs	2
Butter	200 g
Sugar	100 g
Raisins	300 g

Lemon Buns (makes 20)	
Flour	100 g
Eggs	2
Butter	100 g
Sugar	100 g
Lemon	1

    Answer: £ _____

19. Martina has a budget of £120 for her party. A bowling party costs £9.50
    for each child. How many children can Martina afford to have at her party?

    Answer: _____

20. Lucas stacked some 450 g boxes of dog biscuits on a set of scales.
    The total weight was 9 kg. The height of each box was 12.5 cm.
    How tall, in centimetres, was the stack of boxes?

    / 9

    Answer: _____ cm

Data Tables

A school surveyed the types of computers that pupils use at home. The results are shown in the table.

	Laptops	PCs	None
Class A	15	8	6
Class B	14	12	5
Class C	9	17	6

1. How many pupils in class A use a laptop at home?   Answer: _____

2. How many pupils in class B use a PC at home?   Answer: _____

3. In class C, how many more pupils use a PC than use a laptop?   Answer: _____

4. In which class did the greatest number of pupils use a PC?   Answer: _____

5. How many pupils in total did not use a computer at home?   Answer: _____

/ 5

6. 40 children were asked their favourite colour. How many girls chose green?

	Red	Green	Blue
Boys	8	4	8
Girls	5		7

Answer: _____

7. In a recent study, some children were asked how much pocket money they received.

    The results are shown in the table.

    How many children received £3.50 or less?

Amount of pocket money	Number of children
Less than £1	15
Between £1 and £3.50	12
More than £3.50 but less than £5	23
Between £5 and £10	18
More than £10	8

Answer: _____

8. The table shows the number of pizzas sold in one hour.

	Large	Small	Total
Pepperoni	6		8
Cheese and ham		7	
Total		9	24

How many large cheese and ham pizzas were sold?

Answer: _____

/ 3

Displaying Data

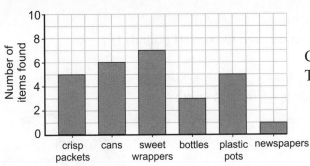

Class 5B carried out a litter survey in their local park. The results are shown in a bar chart.

1. Which item did they find the fewest of?

Answer: _____

2. How many crisp packets did they find?

Answer: _____

3. How many more sweet wrappers were found than bottles?

Answer: _____

4. How many fewer newspapers were found than crisp packets?

Answer: _____

5. Which item was found twice as often as bottles?

Answer: _____

/ 5

6. The pictogram shows the number of fish in an aquarium.

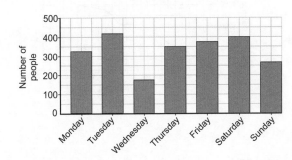

How many Blue Acara fish were in the aquarium?

Answer: _____

7. A cinema has 450 seats. The bar chart shows the number of people who watched the 7 pm film each evening one week.

How many seats were empty on Friday?
Circle the correct answer.

75   125   25   375   50

8. This pictogram shows the number of drinks bought at a school disco.
How many more children bought blackcurrant than cherryade?

Type of drink	Number bought
Orange	
Blackcurrant	
Cherryade	

= 4 drinks

Answer: _____

/ 3

Section Four — Data Handling

Displaying Data

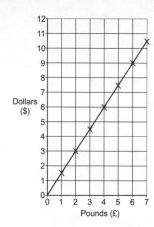

9. This line graph can be used to convert pounds (£) to dollars ($).

How many pounds is 45 dollars worth?

Answer: £ _____

10. A survey asked teenagers about how they spend their pocket money. The results are shown in the pie chart.

18 teenagers said they preferred to spend their pocket money on technology. How many teenagers were interviewed altogether? Circle the correct answer.

75   36   54   72   58

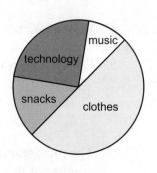

11. This line graph shows the distance travelled by Joe when he took his dog for a walk.

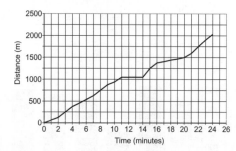

During his walk he stopped to talk to a friend.

How long did they talk for?

Answer: _____ minutes

12. This pie chart shows the proportion of tickets sold for different sports at an athletics event.

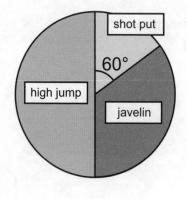

250 tickets were sold for the shot put.
How many tickets were sold for the high jump?

Hint: Compare the sizes of the shot put and high jump sections on the pie chart.

Answer: _____

/ 4

Section Four — Data Handling

Mean, Median, Mode and Range

What is the mode of the following sets of numbers?

1. 6, 6, 8, 5, 10   Answer: _____

2. 17, 19, 18, 12, 19   Answer: _____

3. 14, 18, 17, 18, 15   Answer: _____

4. 4, 6, 8, 3, 4, 3, 2, 3   Answer: _____

5. 10, 11, 19, 18, 14, 19, 12, 19, 17   Answer: _____

 / 5

Give the median of each row of numbers below.

6. 7, 9, 12, 14, 17   Answer: _____

7. 21, 19, 18, 11, 9   Answer: _____

8. 5, 6, 8, 8, 9, 11   Answer: _____

9. 59, 63, 57, 21, 34, 82   Answer: _____

10. 23, 14, 35, 28, 32, 27   Answer: _____

 / 5

11. Bently Rovers scored the following numbers of goals in their matches last season.

    0, 2, 4, 2, 5, 1, 0, 2

    What was the mean number of goals that they scored?   Answer: _____

12. The line graph shows how many chickens hatched each day at Finch Farm.

    What is the range of the number of chickens hatched?

    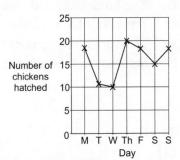

    Answer: _____

13. This table shows the daily temperature (°C) for Weymouth over one week.

	Monday	Tuesday	Wednesday	Thursday	Friday	Saturday	Sunday
High	14	14	10	4	6	11	9
Low	12	6	4	-3	-1	7	6

    Which day had the largest range in temperature?   Answer: _____

14. Here are the results of Phillip's last six spelling tests.

    4, 6, 7, ?, 10, 5

    His mean score was 7. What was the score in his fourth test?

    Answer: _____

    / 4

Section Four — Data Handling

Misleading Data

1. This is a misleading news report.

> **Landslide Victory for Popular Pupil**
>
> Yesterday, there was a landslide victory in a school election between five pupils for the next school representative. Just 12 children chose Anne, ten percent picked Hasim, 25% wanted Jamie to be their representative and 5% voted for Ted. Lex didn't get any votes.

Who became the new school representative?   Answer: _____

2. The pictogram shows the number of animals in a zoo.

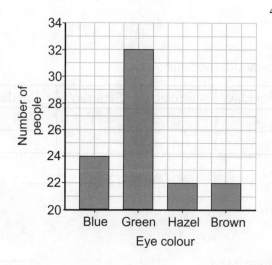

Name of Animal	Number in Zoo

1 picture = 4 animals

Why is the pictogram misleading?
Circle the letter next to the correct answer.

A   It doesn't show other animals in the zoo.
B   The categories are not in order.
C   The pictures are not the same size.
D   There cannot be half a monkey.
E   Not all zoos have the same animals.

3. Which of the statements below describes why this line graph is misleading?
Circle the letter next to the correct answer.

A   It is not a straight line.
B   The horizontal scale is not numbered.
C   The result for Thursday looks wrong.
D   The vertical scale does not go up in even steps.
E   Saturday and Sunday are not included.

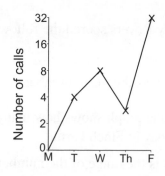

4. This misleading bar chart shows the eye colours of children in Year 6. Which of the following statements is true? Circle the letter next to the correct answer.

A   The number of people with blue eyes is double the number with brown eyes.
B   The number of people with hazel eyes is $\frac{2}{3}$ of the number with blue eyes.
C   The number of people with green eyes is 3 times as many as those with blue eyes.
D   The number of people with blue eyes is $\frac{3}{4}$ of the number with green eyes.
E   The number of people with green eyes is 5 times as many as those with brown eyes.

/ 4

Section Four — Data Handling

Probability

Use the spinner below to answer the following questions.
Write the answers to questions 1 - 3 as a fraction.

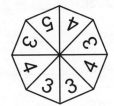

1. What is the probability that
    the spinner will land on 4?

    Answer: _____

2. What is the probability that the
    spinner will land on an odd number?

    Answer: _____

3. What is the probability that the spinner will land on 7?

    Answer: _____

4. Which number is the spinner least likely to land on?

    Answer: _____

5. Which number has an even chance of being spun?

    Answer: _____

/ 5

Write the answers to questions 6 - 9 as a fraction.

6. What is the probability of throwing an even number
    using a dice numbered 1 to 6?

    Answer: _____

7. What is the probability of randomly choosing a red marble
    from a jar containing 5 red, 1 blue and 6 green marbles?

    Answer: _____

8. What is the probability of randomly choosing a green marble
    from a jar containing 2 red, 7 green and 3 blue marbles?

    Answer: _____

9. What is the probability of randomly choosing a striped sock
    from a drawer containing 2 plain, 4 spotty and 3 striped socks?

    Answer: _____

/ 4

10. Letter tiles spelling the word MATHEMATICS are placed
    into a bag. Frankie randomly picks a tile. What is the
    probability of Frankie picking a tile that is not M, S or A?

    Answer: _____

11. A box contains yellow, red and green scarves. Sandra has a $\frac{1}{4}$
    chance of randomly choosing a yellow scarf. If there are 16
    scarves in the box and 5 of them are green, how many are red?

    Answer: _____

12. The table shows the jams made by Mrs Jameson. She
    picked a jar at random. Circle the letter on the probability
    scale that shows the probability of the jam being strawberry.

Variety	Number of jars
Apple	6
Plum	3
Strawberry	4
Raspberry	3

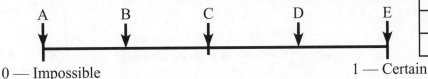

0 — Impossible   1 — Certain

13. A bag of 24 sweets contains equal amounts of mice, bears, snakes and frogs. Grace offers
    the bag to three friends who each take a sweet at random. The first two friends both get a bear.
    What is the probability that the third friend will also get a bear?

    Answer: _____

/ 4

Section Four — Data Handling

Angles

Use the diagram to answer questions 1 to 5.

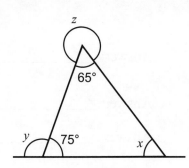

1. Calculate the size of angle *x*.   Answer: _____ °

2. What type of angle is *x*?   Answer: _____

3. Calculate the size of angle *y*.   Answer: _____ °

4. What type of angle is *y*?   Answer: _____

5. Calculate the size of angle *z*.   Answer: _____ °

/ 5

6. Angles A, B and C lie on a straight line.
   What is the total of these three angles?   Answer: _____ °

7. Angles S, T and U lie on a straight line.
   If S is 34° and T is 23°, what is the size of U?   Answer: _____ °

8. A triangle has one right-angle and one angle of 67°.
   What is the size of the other angle?   Answer: _____ °

/ 3

9. Estimate the size of angle *a*. Circle the correct answer.

   75°   45°   15°   90°   125°

10. Which of these shapes contains at least one obtuse angle? Circle the correct answer.

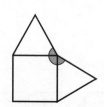

11. Grace drew a shape using a square and two equilateral triangles.
    What is the size of the shaded angle in her shape?

    Answer: _____ °

12. Three of the angles in this quadrilateral measure 85°, 82° and 83°.
    What is the size of angle *y*?

    Hint: Think about the total of the angles in a quadrilateral.

    Answer: _____ °

13. The minute hand on this clock turns 300° clockwise.
    What number is it now pointing to?

    Answer: _____

    / 5

Section Five — Shape and Space

2D Shapes

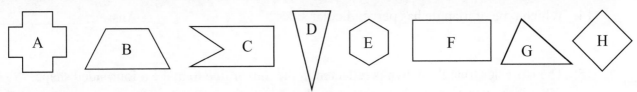

Use the shapes above to answer questions 1-5 below.

1. Which shape has exactly two right angles?   Answer: _____

2. Which shape is an isosceles triangle?   Answer: _____

3. Which shape is a pentagon?   Answer: _____

4. Which quadrilateral has all sides equal in length? Answer: _____

5. Which shape has just one pair of parallel sides and no right angles? Answer: _____

/ 5

This shape is made from a square (BCDE) and an isosceles triangle (ABE).

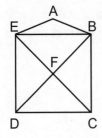

6. Which line is parallel to DE?   Answer: _____

7. Which line is equal in length to AE?   Answer: _____

8. What shape is made by joining points ABFE?   Answer: _____

9. What shape is formed by joining points BCDEF?   Answer: _____

10. Which line is both perpendicular to and the same length as DB? Answer: _____

/ 5

11. Which of these shapes cannot be sorted into any of the cells in this diagram?
    Circle the correct answer.

	Right angles	No right angles
Triangle		
Quadrilateral		

12. Sam has a shape. Sam answers three questions about the shape.
    The diagram below shows the questions and his answers. What shape does he have?

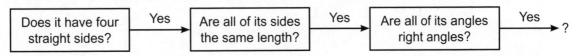

    Answer: _____

13. Which one of the following shapes has exactly one pair of parallel sides?
    Circle the correct answer.

    Square   Rhombus   Kite   Parallelogram   Trapezium

/ 3

Section Five — Shape and Space

2D Shapes

14. Which type of triangle has perpendicular sides?   Answer: _____

15. The isosceles triangle shown is reflected in the mirror line to make a four-sided shape. What is the name of the shape that is made? Circle the correct answer.

    Parallelogram   Trapezium   Rhombus   Kite   Square

    mirror line ⟶

16. James drew a quadrilateral with 2 pairs of parallel sides, a pair of obtuse angles and a pair of acute angles. Each pair of parallel sides are the same length. What shape did he draw?   Answer: _____

17. This traffic sign has a diameter of 900 mm. What is the radius of the sign? Circle the correct answer.

    60

    180 mm   9000 mm   60 mm   1800 mm   450 mm

18. Mr Johnson wants to buy tiles that fit together with other tiles of the same shape without leaving gaps in between them. Which of these tiles should he not choose? Circle the correct answer.

    A   B   C   D   E

19. Which of these regular polygons has the largest internal angle? Circle the correct answer.

    Triangle   Octagon   Pentagon   Hexagon   Square

20. This rhombus has two angles that are both 30°. What size is angle a?

    Answer: _____ °

    30° a 30°

21. Which of the shapes has been placed incorrectly in this Venn diagram? Circle the letter of the correct shape below.

    A   B   C   D   E

    four right angles   at least one pair of equal sides

    A   B   C

    D

    E

    no parallel lines

22. Darma thinks of a shape. It is a quadrilateral with two pairs of equal sides but no parallel sides. One pair of angles is equal. What shape is Darma thinking of?

    Answer: _____

    /9

Section Five — Shape and Space

2D Shapes — Area and Perimeter

Darren drew four shapes onto squared paper. Each square on the paper has sides of 1 cm.

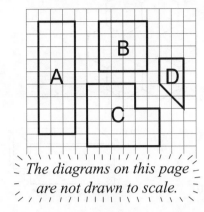

The diagrams on this page are not drawn to scale.

1. What is the area of shape B?   Answer: _____ cm²

2. What is the area of shape C?   Answer: _____ cm²

3. What is the area of shape D?   Answer: _____ cm²

4. What is the perimeter of shape A?   Answer: _____ cm

5. What is the perimeter of shape C?   Answer: _____ cm

/ 5

The dimensions of four shapes are shown.

6. What is the perimeter of shape S?   Answer: _____ cm

7. What is the perimeter of shape R?   Answer: _____ cm

8. What is the perimeter of shape T?   Answer: _____ cm

9. What is the area of shape S?   Answer: _____ cm²

10. What is the area of shape U?   Answer: _____ cm²

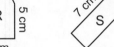

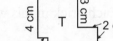

/ 5

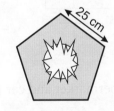

11. A coffee table is in the shape of a regular pentagon. One side is 25 cm in length. What is the perimeter of the table?

    Answer: _____ cm

12. A rectangular carpet has an area of 75 m². It is 15 metres long. How wide is it?

    Answer: _____ m

13. The school playground is a regular octagon. It has a perimeter of 560 m. What is the length of each edge?   Answer: _____ m

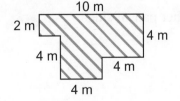

14. The diagram shows the sheep pen being built by Farmer Brown. He wants to enclose the pen completely using 2 m fence panels. How many panels will he need?

    Answer: _____

15. Which two of the shapes that are drawn on the grid have the same area?

    Answer: _____

/ 5

Section Five — Shape and Space

2D Shapes — Area and Perimeter

16. Mr Robinson built a patio using hexagonal slabs.
    The slabs are regular hexagons with a side length of 30 cm.
    What is the perimeter of the patio?

    Answer: _____ cm

17. James built this cardboard tunnel for his toy cars.
    What is the total area of the outside faces of the tunnel?

    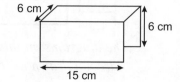

    Answer: _____ cm²

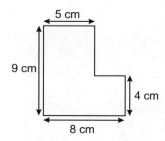

18. Calculate the area of this shape.

    Answer: _____ cm²

19. Each brick in this wall is 5 cm wide and 10 cm long.

    Each brick is exactly centred over the two that it
    rests on. What is the perimeter of the hole in the wall?

    Answer: _____ cm

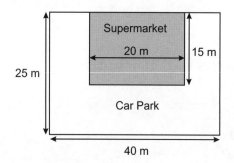

20. The diagram shows a plan of a supermarket and car park.
    What is the area of the car park?

    Answer: _____ m²

21. A rectangle has one pair of sides that are 5 cm longer than the other pair of sides.
    The area of the rectangle is 24 cm². What is its perimeter?

    Answer: _____ cm

22. Martha is painting a room. There are 4 walls that are each 4 m wide and 2 m tall.
    If each tin of paint contains enough paint for 12 m² of wall, how many tins will Martha
    need for the whole room?

    Answer: _____

/ 7

Symmetry

Look carefully at this set of letters and use them to answer questions 1 to 4 below.

W R D H F N

1. How many of the letters have no lines of symmetry?   Answer: _____

2. Which letter has two lines of symmetry?   Answer: _____

3. Which letter only has a vertical line of symmetry?   Answer: _____

4. Which letter only has a horizontal line of symmetry?   Answer: _____

/ 4

5. Which of these triangles has a horizontal line of symmetry? Circle the correct answer.

6. Which of these shapes has rotational symmetry?
    Circle the letter underneath the correct answer.

A   B   C   D   E

Hint: A shape has rotational symmetry if it fits into itself more than once when it is rotated about its centre.

7. Harish reflects the parallelogram on the right in the mirror line to make a new shape.
    What is the shape that Harish makes? Circle the correct answer.

    Triangle   Quadrilateral   Pentagon   Hexagon   Heptagon

8. Look at this shape. How many lines of symmetry does it have?

    Answer: _____

9. Which of the following shapes has a diagonal line of symmetry?
    Circle the letter underneath the correct answer.

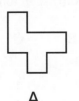 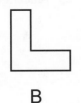 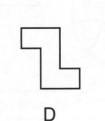 
A   B   C   D   E

/ 5

Section Five — Shape and Space

3D Shapes

Use these 3D shapes to answer questions 1-5 below.

   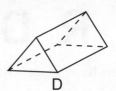

A   B   C   D   E

1. How many rectangular faces does shape A have?   Answer: _____

2. Which shape has six identical faces?   Answer: _____

3. Which shape has five faces and nine edges?   Answer: _____

4. Which shape has fewer edges than faces?   Answer: _____

5. Which shape has five faces, eight edges and five vertices?   Answer: _____

/ 5

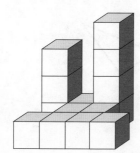

6. Ruth built this shape using 1 cm³ cubes. What is the volume of this shape?

    Answer: _____ cm³

7. What is the largest number of 1 cm³ cubes that will fit into this box?

    Answer: _____

    4 cm   7 cm   3 cm

8. Which of these nets will fold up to form a cube? Circle the correct answer.

A   B   C   D   E

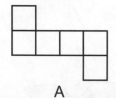 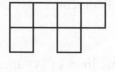 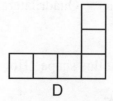 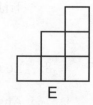

Prism | More than two quadrilateral faces

A B C D E

At least one curved edge

9. Elizabeth is sorting solid shapes using a Venn diagram. In which section should she place a cuboid? Circle the correct answer.

    A   **B**   **C**   **D**   **E**

/ 4

Section Five — Shape and Space

3D Shapes

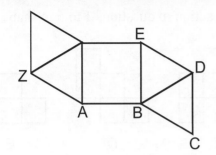

10. Karen folds this net to make a 3D shape.
    Which point joins to corner Z? Circle the correct answer.

    A   B   C   D   E

11. Katie wants to make a cube where all the opposite faces have the same letter.
    Which net must she use? Circle the correct answer.

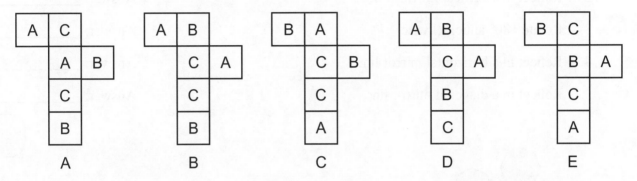

    A   B   C   D   E

12. Ravi is tidying his bedroom. How many cubes with
    edges of length 4 cm can he fit into his toy box?
    Circle the correct answer.

    90   180   406   30   360

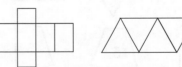

13. Each of these nets can make one of the 3D shapes A-E.
    Which 3D shape does not have a matching net? Circle the correct answer.

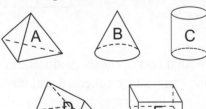
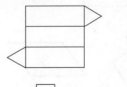
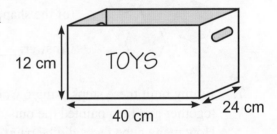
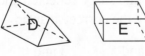

14. A house brick has a volume of 800 cm³. If it is 20 cm long and 5 cm high, how wide is it?

    Answer: _____ cm

15. Peter stacks a cuboid and a cube to make this shape.
    What is the total volume of the shape he has made?

    Answer: _____ m³

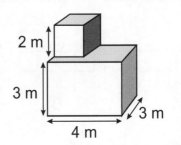

/ 6

Section Five — Shape and Space

Shape Problems

Write down the letter of the shape you would get if you did each action in questions 1 to 5 to shape X.

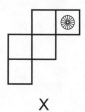 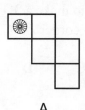 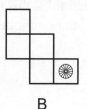 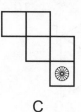 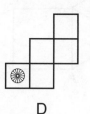 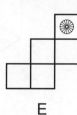

X   A   B   C   D   E

1. Rotate 90° clockwise.   Answer: _____

2. Reflect in a vertical mirror line.   Answer: _____

3. Rotate 180° anticlockwise.   Answer: _____

4. Reflect in a horizontal mirror line.   Answer: _____

5. Reflect in a diagonal mirror line.   Answer: _____

/ 5

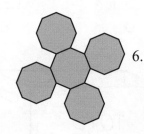

6. This shape is made up of identical regular octagons. The perimeter of the shape is 64 cm. How long is each side of the octagons?

    Answer: _____ cm

7. Jimmy built these steps using 6 wooden cubes. He glued them together and then painted the outside. He did not paint the base. How many cube faces did he paint?

    Hint: Don't forget the faces that you can't see.

    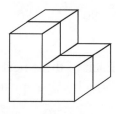

    Answer: _____

8. Which two of these quadrilaterals are exactly the same shape reflected and turned around? Circle the correct answer.

    4 and 5   3 and 6   2 and 6

    1 and 6   1 and 5

9. Fiona and Kim made exactly the same shape using seven cubes. Fiona made shape Z. Which shape did Kim make? Circle the correct answer.

    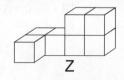

    Z

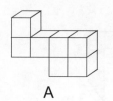 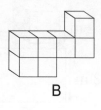 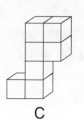 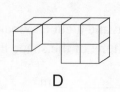 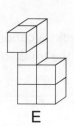

A   B   C   D   E

/ 4

Section Five — Shape and Space

Coordinates

The coordinate grid shows the location of attractions at a fun fair.

Hint: Give the *x*-axis value first when you write coordinates.

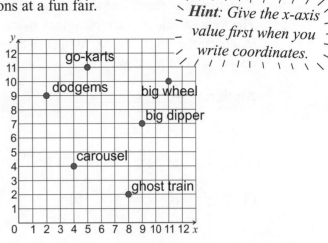

1. What are the coordinates of the big dipper?

    Answer: _____

2. What are the coordinates of the go-karts?

    Answer: _____

3. What are the coordinates of the carousel?

    Answer: _____

4. What are the coordinates of the ghost train?   Answer: _____

5. What are the coordinates of the dodgems?   Answer: _____

/ 5

6. Ted starts at point A. He moves 4 squares west
    and then 7 squares north. What are the coordinates
    of the point he finishes at?

    Answer: _____

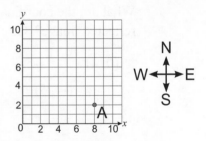

7. A line LM is drawn on the grid parallel
    to the line JK.

    What could the coordinates of point L be?
    Circle the correct answer.

    (−7, 0)   (−1, 0)   (5, −2)

        (7, 0)   (0, −1)

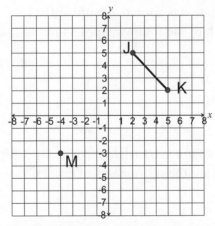

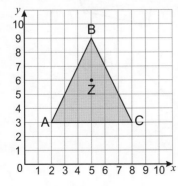

8. The triangle on the grid is rotated 90° clockwise about point Z.
    What are the new coordinates of corner B?

    Answer: _____

/ 3

Section Five — Shape and Space

Coordinates

9. A rectangle is drawn onto a coordinate grid. The longest side of the rectangle is twice the length of the shortest side. What are the coordinates of point W?

   Answer: _____

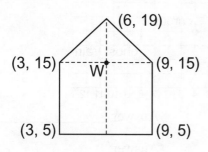

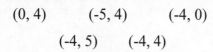

10. A pentagon is drawn on a grid. The coordinates of its corners are given. Two lines are drawn on the pentagon. What are the coordinates of their intersection, W?

    Answer: _____

11. Charlie drew a shape onto a coordinate grid. He reflected his shape in the mirror line shown. What are the coordinates of point G on the reflected image? Circle the correct answer.

    (0, 4)   (-5, 4)   (-4, 0)

    (-4, 5)   (-4, 4)

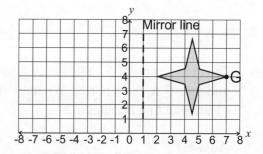

12. A square has corners positioned at (2, 2), (2, 7), (7, 7) and (7, 2). Which of the following points lies outside of the shape? Circle the correct answer.

    (3, 6)   (5, 4)   (8, 4)   (2, 3)   (7, 6)

13. A pentagon is translated to a new position as shown. What are the coordinates of point C?

    Answer: _____

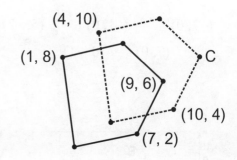

14. What are the coordinates of point C which is exactly half way between points A and B?

    Answer: _____

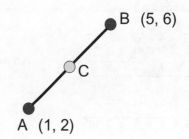

Section Five — Shape and Space

/ 6

Units

| km | cm | m | mm |

Which of the units above would you choose to measure the following?

1.   The length of a pencil.   Answer: _____

2.   The distance between London and Liverpool.   Answer: _____

3.   The height of a door.   Answer: _____

4.   The thickness of a coin.   Answer: _____

/ 4

5.   Tom bought a melon with a mass of 1.56 kilograms.
     What is the mass of the melon in grams?   Answer: _____ g

6.   A jug holds 2.5 litres.
     How many millilitres is this?   Answer: _____ ml

7.   Juan is 128 centimetres tall.
     How tall is he in metres?   Answer: _____ m

8.   Tracy walks 15.3 kilometres.
     How many metres did she walk?   Answer: _____ m

9.   A bucket contains 4500 grams of sand.
     What is the mass of the sand in kilograms?   Answer: _____ kg

/ 5

10. Which of the following is the most likely mass of a pencil?
     Circle the correct answer.

         5.4 kg   5400 g   5.4 g   54 kg   2.54 kg

11. Look at the weighing scale on the right.
     What is the weight of this parcel in grams?

     Answer: _____ g

12. Which container will hold about 1 litre of water?
     Circle the correct answer.

     egg cup   teacup   dustbin   saucepan   teaspoon

13. Electric cable is sold in rolls of 14 m. Sam wants
     1.4 km of cable. How many rolls does he need to buy?   Answer: _____

14. Farmer Jones fills 32 bags with carrots. Each bag contains the
     same mass of carrots. The total mass of the carrots is 16 kg.
     What mass of carrots is in each bag?

/ 5

     Answer: _____ g

Units

15. Mrs Scott went shopping for ribbon. She bought 650 cm of red ribbon, 7.6 m of blue ribbon and 12.3 m of green ribbon. How many metres of ribbon did she buy altogether?

Answer: _____ m

16. An acorn is approximately 6 cm tall. It grows into an oak tree which is 300 times the height of the acorn. How tall is the oak tree?

Answer: _____ m

17. Gracie bought a 1.5 litre bottle of bubble bath. After 3 baths she had used 400 ml. Which diagram best shows how much she has left? Circle the correct answer.

A   B   C   D   E

18. How many litres of liquid can you fit into eight 750 ml bottles?

Answer: _____ l

19. A factory produces 42 packets of cereal every hour. Each packet of cereal weighs 250 g. How many kilograms of cereal is produced in one hour? Circle the correct answer.

    A 48 kg   **B** 168 kg   **C** 10.5 kg   **D** 21 kg   **E** 84 kg

20. Mrs Tan has a full 2 litre bottle of lemonade. She pours twelve 150 ml glasses of lemonade. How much lemonade does she have left in the bottle?

Answer: _____ ml

21. Mrs Conway visits her daughter who lives 270 km away. She can travel 9 km on $\frac{1}{2}$ a litre of petrol. How many litres of petrol did she use to get to her daughter's house?

Answer: _____ l

22. Roberto travels by taxi while he's on holiday. He travels 24 km to the waterfall, 15 km to the caverns and 12 km to visit a castle. The taxi charges 25p for every 500 m he travels. What was the total cost of Roberto's taxi ride?

Answer: £_____

23. A hospital's kitchen staff are cooking lunch for the patients. They cook 4 kg of meatballs and twice that weight of pasta. Each lunch serving of meatballs and pasta weighs 250 g. How many servings can they make? Circle the correct answer.

    A 32   **B** 16   **C** 40   **D** 48   **E** 56

24. Large paper clips are 3 cm long and small ones are 15 mm. James lays out 400 small paper clips and 250 large paper clips end-to-end in a row. How long was the row of paper clips in metres?

Answer: _____ m

/ 10

Section Six — Units and Measures

Time

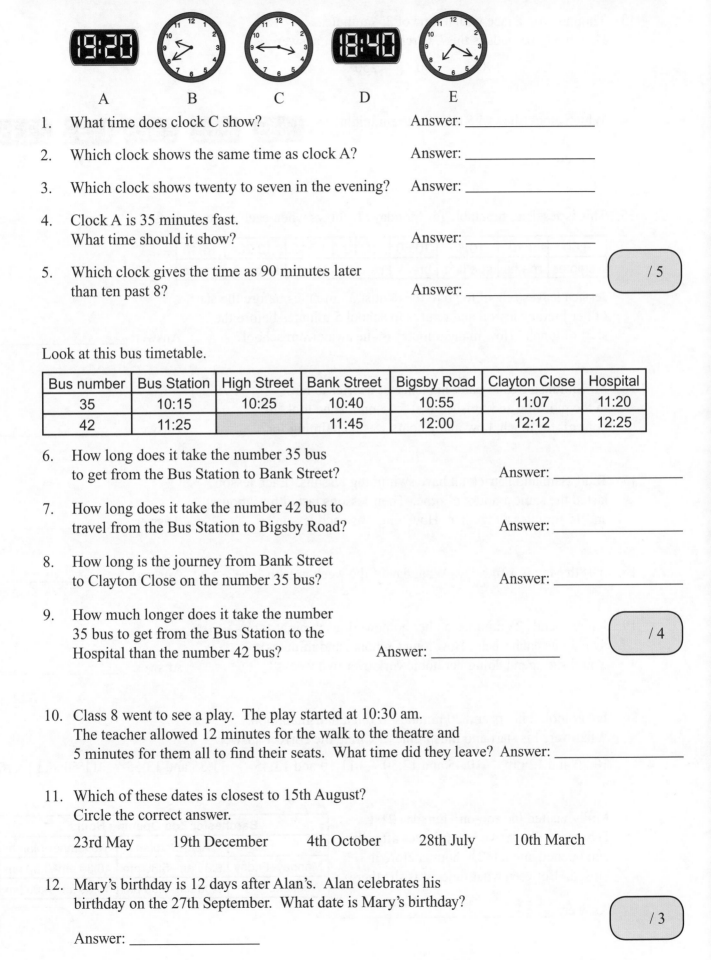

A   B   C   D   E

1. What time does clock C show?   Answer: _____

2. Which clock shows the same time as clock A?   Answer: _____

3. Which clock shows twenty to seven in the evening?   Answer: _____

4. Clock A is 35 minutes fast.
    What time should it show?   Answer: _____

5. Which clock gives the time as 90 minutes later
    than ten past 8?   Answer: _____   / 5

Look at this bus timetable.

Bus number	Bus Station	High Street	Bank Street	Bigsby Road	Clayton Close	Hospital
35	10:15	10:25	10:40	10:55	11:07	11:20
42	11:25		11:45	12:00	12:12	12:25

6. How long does it take the number 35 bus
    to get from the Bus Station to Bank Street?   Answer: _____

7. How long does it take the number 42 bus to
    travel from the Bus Station to Bigsby Road?   Answer: _____

8. How long is the journey from Bank Street
    to Clayton Close on the number 35 bus?   Answer: _____

9. How much longer does it take the number
    35 bus to get from the Bus Station to the
    Hospital than the number 42 bus?   Answer: _____   / 4

10. Class 8 went to see a play. The play started at 10:30 am.
    The teacher allowed 12 minutes for the walk to the theatre and
    5 minutes for them all to find their seats. What time did they leave? Answer: _____

11. Which of these dates is closest to 15th August?
    Circle the correct answer.

    23rd May   19th December   4th October   28th July   10th March

12. Mary's birthday is 12 days after Alan's. Alan celebrates his
    birthday on the 27th September. What date is Mary's birthday?

    Answer: _____   / 3

Section Six — Units and Measures

Time

13. Thomas won a race with a time of $3\frac{3}{4}$ minutes.
    How many seconds is this? Circle the correct answer.

    225   190   300   250   45

14. Which clock shows 25 minutes to midnight?

    11:35   12:25   23:25   11:25   23:35
    A   B   C   D   E

    Answer: _____

15. This is Jessica's timetable for Monday. It shows when each activity starts.

9:00	9:10	10:15	10:50	11:10	12:15	13:20	14:40
register	maths	spelling	break	literacy	lunch	science	music

    Jessica leaves school to go to the dentist 35 minutes before the start
    of her literacy lesson and returns to school 5 minutes before the
    start of lunch. How many minutes is she away from school?   Answer: _____

16. Mr Smith started to paint his fence at quarter to ten
    in the morning and finished it at 5.15 pm. If he took an
    hour off for lunch, how many hours was he painting for?   Answer: _____

17. Todd, Sam and Patrick all have swimming lessons. Each lesson
    lasted the same amount of time. Their lessons lasted for 2 hours
    and 15 minutes altogether. How long was each lesson?   Answer: _____

18. If 18th May is a Tuesday. What day of the week is 18th June?   Answer: _____

19. Jenny spends 25 minutes on her homework each night for
    five nights each week. How long (in hours and minutes)
    would she spend doing her homework over two weeks?   Answer: _____

20. Javier took 2 hours and 20 minutes to run a half-marathon.
    What were his start and finish times? Circle the correct answer.

    10:20 and 12:00   10:45 and 12:50   11:10 and 13:45   11:35 and 13:55   11:50 and 13:10

21. Molly visited the zoo on Thursday 21st
    February. She arrived 40 minutes after the
    zoo opened and left $2\frac{1}{2}$ hours before it
    closed. Between what times was she there?

Barchester Zoo Opening Hours		
	April–October	November–March
Monday–Friday	9:30 am–5:30 pm	10:30 am–3:30 pm
Weekend	9:00 am–6:00 pm	10:30 am–4:00 pm

    Answer: _____

    / 9

Mixed Problems

1. 60 people were asked what colour car they drove.
    The results were recorded in a pie chart.
    What percentage drove black or silver cars?

    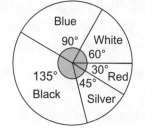

    Answer: _____ %

2. Greg has a bag of peanuts. He eats $\frac{1}{20}$ of the
    bag each day. How many days will it take
    him to eat 40 % of the bag of peanuts?   Answer: _____

3. Class 6B wrote down which flavour of pie was their
    favourite. They showed their results in a pictogram.
    What is the modal flavour of pie?

Flavour of Pie	Number of People
Pecan	🥧🥧◖
Apple	🥧🥧🥧
Rhubarb	🥧
Pumpkin	🥧◖
Blueberry	🥧🥧🥧🥧

    🥧 = 2 people

    Answer: _____

4. Jacob buys a bag of seeds for £4.50. Each morning he
    puts out two cups of seeds on his bird table. The bag runs
    out after 9 days. How much does one cup of seeds cost?   Answer: _____ p

5. Miss Orchard is buying some carpet for her hallway, which is 6 m
    long and 1.5 m wide. The carpet she has chosen costs £22 per
    square metre. How much will it cost to carpet her hallway in total?   Answer: £ _____

6. Mr Phillips filled a swimming pool with water from a hose.
    20 litres of water went into the pool every minute the hose was
    turned on. Mr Phillips turned the hose on at 8:20 am and turned
    it off at 10 am. How many litres of water did he put into the pool?   Answer: _____ l

7. 1 m by 1 m patio slabs cost £6.00 each. Mr Taylor's patio is 8 m long and 4 m
    wide. How much will it cost him to pave his patio? Circle the correct answer.

    A £60   **B** £124   **C** £160   **D** £192   **E** £224

8. The picture on the right shows the angle on a straight line split into 3 parts.
    What fraction of the total does angle x represent? Circle the correct answer.

    $\frac{1}{2}$ $\frac{1}{4}$ $\frac{1}{5}$ $\frac{1}{6}$ $\frac{1}{3}$

    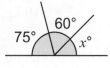

9. Mrs Farooq records the size of her gas bill
    on a bar chart. The mean of her four bills
    is £80. How much is her bill in April?

    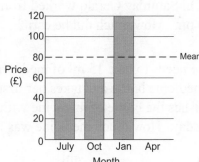

    Answer: £ _____

    / 9

Mixed Problems

10. Yussif filled this container with 1000 cm³ of water.
What percentage of the container was filled with water?
Circle the correct answer.

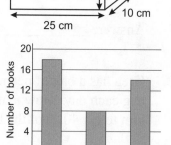

10 cm
10 cm
25 cm

30 %   15 %   40 %   25 %   20 %

11. 40 language textbooks were put into a box. The number of
books for each subject was recorded in a bar chart. Circle
the probability of picking a German book from the box.

A ⅓   B ⅕   C ⁴⁄₁₀   D ⁸⁄₂₀   E ¼

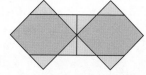

12. Lars is cleaning his windows. He has a bucket which can
hold 6 litres of water and a 600 ml bottle of washing liquid.
He needs to add 5 ml of washing liquid to every 500 ml of
water that he uses. How many full buckets of water could
he mix with washing liquid before the bottle ran out?

Answer: _____

13. Hannah has some tiles in two different shapes, squares
and hexagons. She cuts some of the square tiles in
half to make triangles and makes a pattern. What is
the area of her pattern? Circle the correct answer.

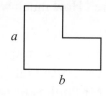

Area = S Area = H

Hannah's Pattern

$2H + 8S$ $2H + 4S$ $2H + 2S$ $H + 4S$ $H + 2S$

14. What is the perimeter of this shape?
Circle the correct answer.

$2a + 2b$ $a + b$ $a \times b$ $2a \times 2b$ $2a + b - ab$

a
b

15. Circle the rule below that gives this sequence:
        5,   12,   19,   26,   33...

A $n + 7$ B $7n - 2$ C $7n + 2$ D $n + 4$ E $n + n^2$

16. Mr Drew weighed the crops from each of his five apple trees.
He worked out that the mean crop weight was 320 kg. The
crops from four of his trees were 370 kg, 280 kg, 330 kg and
310 kg. What was the weight of the crop from the fifth tree?

Answer: _____ kg

17. Gerald is paid £3.50 for every half hour of work he
does. On Saturday Gerald worked from 6:20 am
to 4:50 pm. How much did he earn?

Answer: £ _____

18. Melanie needs to take 15 ml of medicine every 2 hours. She opens
a full medicine bottle and takes her first dose at 4 pm on Monday,
and finishes the bottle of medicine with a last dose at 2 pm on
Wednesday. How much medicine was in the bottle to start with?

Hint: Don't forget the dose at the start and at the end.

/ 9

Answer: _____ ml

Assessment Test 1

The rest of the book contains four full-length assessment tests, to help you improve your maths skills. Allow 50 minutes to do each test and work as quickly and as carefully as you can.

You can print **multiple-choice answer sheets** for these questions from our website — go to www.cgplearning.co.uk/11+. If you'd prefer to answer them in standard write-in format, either write your answers in the spaces provided or circle the **correct answer** from the options **A** to **E**.

1. James saves the following notes and coins from his pocket money. How much has he saved altogether?

    A £7.80   **C** £78.00   **E** £70.80

    B £7.08   **D** £70.08

    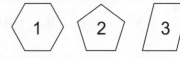

2. A train timetable is shown on the right. If Cara catches the first available train after 9:00 am from Chapel Street, what time will she arrive in Lanston?   Answer: _____

Colwyn Gardens	08:50	09:10	09:30
Chapel Street	08:55	09:15	09:35
Bispham	09:06	09:26	09:46
Torsway	09:17	09:37	09:57
Lanston	09:45	10:05	10:25

3. Bethany cuts her birthday cake into eight equal pieces. What fraction of the cake is one piece?

    A $\frac{1}{7}$ **B** $\frac{1}{8}$ **C** $\frac{1}{6}$ **D** $\frac{6}{7}$ **E** $\frac{7}{8}$

4. Which pair of shapes on the right both have at least one right angle?

    A 1 and 2   **D** 5 and 6

    B 3 and 5   **E** 2 and 4

    C 1 and 6

    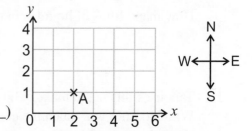

5. Which of these times is the same as 16:50?

    A Ten to five in the morning   **D** Ten to six in the afternoon

    B Ten to four in the afternoon   **E** Ten to six in the morning

    C Ten to five in the afternoon

6. Kaye follows a route from point A on the grid. She walks 1 square north then 2 squares east.

    What are the coordinates of the point her route takes her to?   Answer: (____,____)

7. Robert has two identical trapezium-shaped tiles. One is shown here:

    He arranges the tiles on a triangle dotty grid. Which shape on the right cannot be made without overlapping the tiles?   Answer: _____

    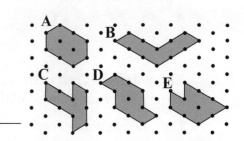

8. What is the missing number in this equation?

    $2808 + 2808 + 2808 = \boxed{} \times 6$ Answer: _____

    / 8

Carry on to the next question →→

9. A bag of fruit costs 99p.
   How much will 9 bags of fruit cost?   Answer: £ _____

10. 24 children want to go camping. 5 children can sleep in each tent.
    How many tents do they need?
                                        Answer: _____

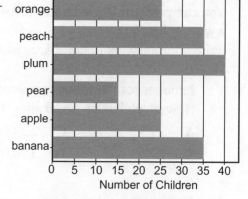

11. Each child in Ella's year group was asked to pick their
    favourite fruit. The results were collected in a bar chart.
    How many more children chose plums than pears?

    A 27   **B** 30   **C** 23   **D** 25   **E** 40

12. What is 10 – 8.93?   Answer: _____

13. Year 5 and Year 6 are split into red, yellow and blue teams.

    The number of points won by each team are shown in the table.
    How many points did the blue team win in total?

                            Answer: _____

Team	Year 5	Year 6	Total
Red	27	50	77
Yellow	32	25	57
Blue		30	
Total	90	105	

14. What is 45.952 rounded to the nearest tenth?

    A 45.9   **B** 46.0   **C** 45.95   **D** 45.96   **E** 45.10

15. This pie chart shows the colours of the sun hats worn by
    36 children. Estimate the number of children wearing yellow hats.

    A 5   **B** 9   **C** 12   **D** 15   **E** 2

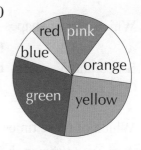

16. Toby has 4.4 litres of lemonade, 0.9 litres of lime juice and
    2.8 litres of orange juice. He mixes them together in a bucket.

    How many litres of liquid is in the bucket?

                            Answer: _____ l

17. Tara uses this net to make a 3D shape.
    Which corner will touch the corner marked X
    when the net is folded?

    A   **B**   **C**   **D**   **E**

18. The table shows part of the information written on a
    tin of fruit. Amrit eats ¾ of the tin of fruit.

    How many grams of carbohydrate did Amrit eat?

    Answer: _____ g

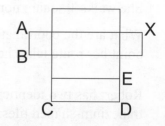

	Per ¼ tin
Protein	0.4 g
Carbohydrate	12.2 g
Fat	0.1 g
Fibre	1.2 g

/ 10

Carry on to the next question →→

19. A packet of 6 Milky Bears costs 40p. They are on special offer
    at 10% off. What is the cost of one milky bear?

    Answer: _____ p

20. Which of the following statements is correct?

    A   The spinner is more likely to land on a grey segment than a black one.
    B   The spinner is twice as likely to land on a spotty segment than a white one.
    C   There is an even chance of the spinner landing on a spotty segment.
    D   The spinner is more likely to land on a spotty segment than any other.
    E   It is impossible for the spinner to land on a black segment.

    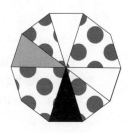

21. Which of the following is equal to 24.

    A $48 - 8 \times 3$ C 3×7 E $2 + 4 \times 4$
    B $3 + 11 \times 2$ D $24 \div 2 - 1$

22. Which of the following shapes could only go in the region labelled X?

    A   rhombus   D   scalene triangle
    B   kite   E   isosceles triangle
    C   regular pentagon

	At least two angles equal	All angles different
At least two sides equal		
All sides different lengths		X

23. Which of the following numbers is not divisible by 4?

    A   324   B   116   C   288   D   132   E   138

24. Joel weighs a basket containing 7 peaches, as shown on the right.
    Each peach weighs 200 g.

    How many kilograms does the basket weigh?

    Answer: _____ kg

25. Here are the shoe sizes of the children at a party.

    6   6   4   8   7   5   7   6   5

    What is the median shoe size?   Answer: _____

26. The shape on the right is a regular hexagon.
    What size is angle *y*?

    A   180°   B   60°   C   120°   D   90°   E   175°

27. The graph shows two sets of spelling scores
    for a group of children.

    What were the scores for the child who had
    a difference of 2 marks on the tests?

    A   10 and 8   C   8 and 6   E   6 and 4
    B   9 and 7   D   7 and 5

    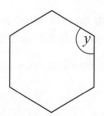

28. What number is the arrow pointing to on the number line?

    24   26   Answer: _____

    / 10

    Carry on to the next question → →

    Assessment Test 1

29. The playground at Jay's school is made up
   of four identical right-angled triangles.
   What is the area of the playground?   Answer: _____ m²

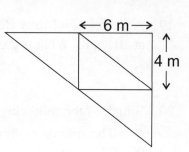

30. Adam thinks of a number.
   He multiplies it by 8, adds 6 and then divides it by 2.
   He ends up with 131.
   What was the number he started with?   Answer: _____

31. Dee is trying to guess what shape Fran is thinking of. Which of
   these clues would be incorrect for Fran's shape shown on the right?

   A   My shape has exactly twelve corners.
   B   My shape has exactly four internal 90° angles.
   C   My shape has exactly eight internal 90° angles.
   D   My shape has twelve sides.
   E   My shape has exactly two lines of symmetry.

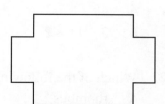

32. The graph on the right shows how many of a particular board
   game have been sold each month over a 6 month period.

   Which of the games below could this be?

	Jan	Feb	Mar	Apr	May	June
Ant Alliance	50	25	10	5	20	45
Bee Bash	45	40	35	30	20	20
Croc Chase	20	10	15	25	40	40
Dodo Detective	30	35	30	35	30	30
Emu Escape	15	20	25	30	40	40

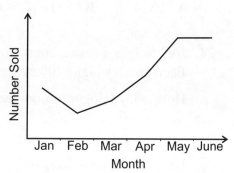

   Answer: _____

33. Amanda has some pocket money.
   She spends 60% of it and is left with £6.00.

   How much money did she start off with?   Answer: £ _____

34. This honeycomb pattern is made up of regular hexagons.
   The length of each side of the hexagons is 2 cm.

   Calculate the distance around the outer edge of this shape.

                           Answer: _____ cm

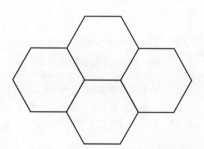

35. A tap is dripping water at a rate of 20 ml per minute.

   How long will it take, to the nearest minute, for 1 litre
   of water to be leaked from the tap?

                           Answer: _____ mins

Carry on to the next question → →

36. On Tuesday the temperature is 1 °C.
By Wednesday it has dropped to –2 °C.

The temperature drops by twice as much from Wednesday
to Thursday. What is the temperature on Thursday?

Answer: _____ °C

37. Eve is baking cupcakes using the ingredients on the right.

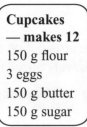

Cupcakes
— makes 12
150 g flour
3 eggs
150 g butter
150 g sugar

Eve needs to make exactly 40 cakes.
How much butter will she need?   Answer: _____ g

38. The rectangle on the coordinate grid is moved 3 units to the right
and 2 units down. What are the new coordinates of its corners?

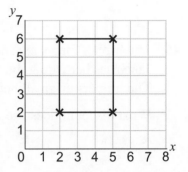

A   (3, 6), (6, 6), (6, 2), (3, 2)
B   (6, 3), (6, 6), (2, 6), (2, 3)
C   (5, 6), (8, 6), (8, 2), (5, 2)
D   (5, 4), (8, 4), (8, 0), (5, 0)
E   (4, 5), (4, 8), (0, 8), (0, 5)

39. A shop sells a different pie and a different dessert each weekday.
Dan only likes meat pies. He hates apple desserts.

If Dan visits the shop on a random weekday, what is the
probability that he will like the pie and dessert on offer?

A $\frac{2}{5}$ B $\frac{3}{5}$ C $\frac{5}{2}$ D $\frac{1}{2}$ E $\frac{6}{10}$

	Pie	Dessert
Monday	beef	lemon cake
Tuesday	mushroom	apple crumble
Wednesday	chicken	apple pie
Thursday	cheese	trifle
Friday	lamb	carrot cake

40. The picture on the right shows a cube on top of a
cuboid. What is the total volume of the shapes?

Answer: _____ cm³

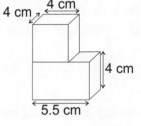

4 cm   4 cm
4 cm
5.5 cm

41. What is the nth term of this sequence?

   3   8   13   18   23

A $6n - 3$ C $4n - 2$ E $5n - 2$
B $2n + 1$ D $5n + 1$

42. A number is written on each face of the triangle-based
pyramid shown on the right. The mean of the numbers is 4.
What are the two hidden numbers?

A   2 and 4   C   2 and 5   E   1 and 4
B   1 and 2   D   1 and 5

43. Bobby's school have been collecting 2p coins for charity.
They count the coins into £1 piles and decide to check they
are correct by weighing the piles. Each coin weighs 7.5 g.
How many grams should each pile weigh?

Answer: _____ g

/ 8

Carry on to the next question → →
Assessment Test 1

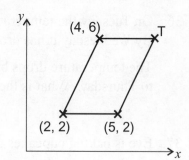

44. The diagram shows a parallelogram.
    What are the coordinates of point T?   Answer: (____,____)

45. Kate starts out on a 135 km journey at 8:50 am.
    She travels on average at 60 km per hour.

    What time does she arrive at her destination?

    Answer: _____

46. Jane works for a shoe shop and is given a discount card.
    Jane uses her card to buy a pair of trainers for £24.75.
    The trainers originally cost £27.50.

    What discount does she receive?

    A 2%   **C** 10%   **E** 25%
    B 5%   **D** 20%

47. The pictogram shows the types of pets owned by children
    in Year 6. Why is this pictogram misleading?

    A The pictures only show one breed of each animal.
    B You cannot have half a fish or half a hamster as a pet.
    C The symbols that represent the different animals are different sizes.
    D There are no rabbits shown on the pictogram.
    E Children in other year groups may own different pets.

    Answer: _____

    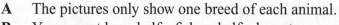

    Fish
    Hamsters
    Cats
    Dogs

    Each symbol = 2 pets

48. A shop has an offer on greetings cards. You can buy 3 boxes
    of 20 cards for the price of 2. A box costs £3.90.

    Bella buys 6 boxes in the offer. She also buys a box of 12
    cards for £1.80. How much does she spend in total?

    Answer: £ _____

49. Use the formula below to find the size of angle m if $n = 46°$.

    $$m = (180 - n) \div 2.$$

    Answer: _____ °

50. A repair engineer charges a customer £50 for every job and £25
    for every hour that he works. Which formula could you use to
    find how much he charges, C, for h hours of work?

    A $C = 50 \div 25h$ **C** $C = 50h - 25$ **E** $C = 50 \times h$
    B $C = 50 + 25h$ **D** $C = 25 + 50h$

/ 7

Assessment Test 2

Allow 50 minutes to do this test. Work as quickly and as carefully as you can.

You can print **multiple-choice answer sheets** for these questions from our website — go to www.cgplearning.co.uk/11+. If you'd prefer to answer them in standard write-in format, either write your answers in the spaces provided or circle the **correct answer** from the options **A** to **E**.

1. This circle has been split into equal parts. What fraction has been shaded?

    A ⅝   **B** ⅓   **C** ⁶⁄₉   **D** ⅜   **E** ⁶⁄₁₈

2. Which of the following is most likely to be
    the weight of a small can of baked beans?

    A 250 g   **B** 2.5 kg   **C** 2.5 g   **D** 2500 g   **E** 25 g

3. The diagram shows a rectangular flag. It is split into four
    equal rectangles. What is the area of the shaded rectangle?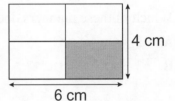

    A 6 cm²   **C** 12 cm²   **E** 20 cm²

    B 10 cm²   **D** 24 cm²

4. Bill goes to a car rally. He keeps a note of the race times
    of the cars in minutes:

    122, 133, 142, 154, 122, 156, 134

    What is the range of the times?

    Answer: _____ minutes

5. Tahsin is doing a shape puzzle. Which of the pieces
    below will complete the puzzle?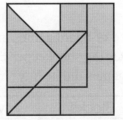

    A   **B**   **C**   **D**   **E**

6. The grid shows a small island. Adam goes for a walk
    starting at (–3, –2). He travels four squares north and
    two squares east. What are the coordinates of the point
    that he reaches?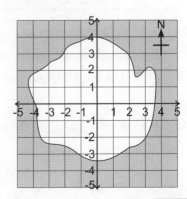

    Answer: (___ , ___)

7. Which of these numbers is 21²?

    A 42   **B** 441   **C** 4410   **D** 4200   **E** 44110

/ 7

Carry on to the next question → →

8. David has a shaded pentagon and a clear pentagon. He places the clear pentagon on top of the shaded one and then rotates it by 180°. What shape does David make?

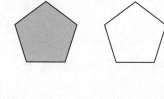

    A   B   C   D   E

9. What number is halfway between 45.6 and 45.9?

    A   45.75   B   45.80   C   45.65   D   45.85   E   45.70

10. Sarinder asked her classmates what their favourite pet was. She recorded her results in the pictogram. How many more people liked dogs than fish?

    Answer: _____

Cat	
Dog	
Fish	
Mouse	

= 4 people

11. Which of these numbers does not divide into 90?

    A   2   C   5   E   9
    B   3   D   7

12. Mr Attenbar lives in the Arctic. He returned to his cabin at 1 pm and put the fire on. After a while he went outside and forgot to close the door behind him. He then came back in and closed the door again.

    This graph shows the temperature inside the cabin. What time did he go outside?

    Answer: _____

13. The price of board games in a shop is shown in the table. Jack gives the shopkeeper £30.00 and gets 50p change. Which games did he buy?

Blocks	Trivia Time	Clueless	Scramble	Brainium
£12.50	£10.50	£6.50	£11.50	£9.50

    A   Scramble, Blocks and Trivia Time   D   Scramble, Blocks and Clueless
    B   Clueless, Brainium and Trivia Time   E   Scramble, Clueless and Trivia Time
    C   Blocks, Clueless and Trivia Time

14. Which of these dials shows 750 g?

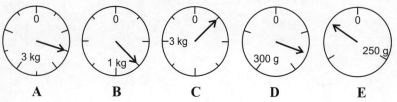

    A   B   C   D   E

/7

Carry on to the next question →→

15. Where does the number 26 belong in this sorting table?

	Even numbers	Odd numbers
Multiples of 3	18 12	3 15
Multiples of 7	28 14	7 49

A top left hand box **D** bottom right hand box

B bottom left hand box **E** none of these

C top right hand box

16. 50 people were asked what colour their car was. 16 people said blue. What percentage of people did not say blue?

Answer: _____%

17. Which of these calculations will give an odd number as the answer?

A 113×115 **C** 436×812 **E** $672 + 998$

B 142×623 **D** $147 + 189$

18. A scarf is 45 cm long. Jade buys 20 scarves.
What is the total length of the scarves?

A 90 m **B** 600 cm **C** 9 m **D** 14 m **E** 450 cm

19. The table shows the number of prizes won by Ester at Bingo in a week.

Ester won 32 prizes altogether. How many prizes did she win on Thursday?

Answer: _____

Day	Number of prizes
Monday	5
Tuesday	8
Wednesday	4
Thursday	
Friday	6

20. Harry paints a large flag on the side of his house. He uses 3 litres of red paint, 4 litres of blue paint and 5 litres of white paint. What percentage of the paint was red?

Answer: _____%

21. Fiona arranges 6 equilateral triangles to make the shape shown. What is the size of the shaded angle?

Answer: _____ °

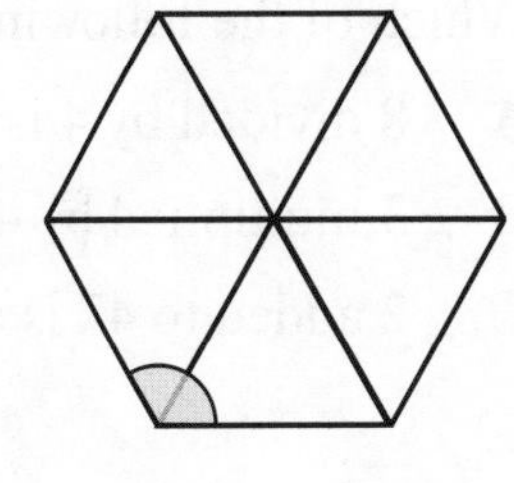

22. Carrie buys 4 chocolate bars at 49p each, and 7 bags of peanuts at 29p each. How much does she spend in total?

A £1.96 **B** £2.03 **C** £3.99 **D** £4.90 **E** £4.10

23. Ten children in Class 6 were asked to give their favourite colour.
The results are written in this list:

red, blue, green, silver, purple, red, gold, gold, green, red

What is the modal colour?

Answer: _____

/ 9

Carry on to the next question $\rightarrow \rightarrow$

Assessment Test 2

24. Lucy has some paper circles and some paper squares which she uses to make a rocket. She cuts some of the shapes in half. The squares have sides of 4 cm and the circles have areas of 10 cm². What is the area of her rocket?

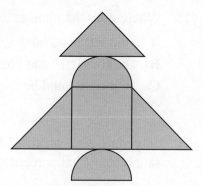

Answer: _____ cm²

25. Elsa has a bag of sweets containing 7 chocolate drops, 8 toffees and 3 liquorice laces.

She takes out 2 sweets at random and eats them. They are both chocolate drops. What is the probability of her randomly picking a toffee next time?

A ³⁄₈   **B** ½   **C** ¾   **D** ⅕   **E** ⁸⁄₁₈

26. Mrs Burton often catches the bus from her home into town. Sometimes she takes bus A, and sometimes she takes bus B. The first stop is outside her house and the last stop is in town. How long does the longest bus ride take?

A   112 minutes   **C**   69 minutes   **E**   59 minutes

B   99 minutes   **D**   72 minutes

Bus A	Bus B
09:44	11:39
09:52	11:45
10:31	12:16
10:56	12:48

27. A plant grows 0.025 m every 6 months. It is 1.5 m tall. How many years will it take to reach 2 m?

Answer: _____

28. Ben places a mirror on the *y*-axis of this graph. What are the coordinates of the reflected point A?

A   (3, 2)   **C**   (1, 4)   **E**   (2, 2)

B   (−2, −2)   **D**   (3, 0)

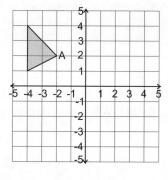

29. Which of the following statements is incorrect?

A   8 divided by 4 is a prime number.   **D**   64 divided by 16 is a square number.

B   3 multiplied by 44 is an odd number.   **E**   11² is an odd number.

C   2 added to 47 is a multiple of 7.

30. 40 girls and boys played in a football tournament. The number of goals and saves made during the tournament were recorded in the table.

How many saves were made in total?

Answer: _____

	Girls	Boys	Total
Goals		4	
Saves	14		
Total	24		44

31. Bernard is running from Land's End to John O'Groats. The distance is 874 miles. If he runs 25 miles a day, how many days will it take him to run the distance?

A   36   **B**   27   **C**   32   **D**   35   **E**   26

/ 8

Carry on to the next question →→

32. The diagram shows three of the angles on a kite.
What is the size of angle a?

Answer: _____ °

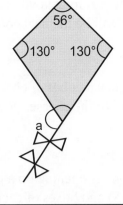

33. | 23 × 14 = 322 |

What is 46 × 140?

A 1288   **C** 64 400   **E** 12 888

B 3220   **D** 6440

34. Raj is buying 2 family tickets for a concert.
How much does he spend?

Answer: £_____

Concert Tickets
Adults   £3.50
Children   £1.50
20% discount for family ticket
(2 adults and 2 children)

35. Which of the following statements is true?

A $\frac{7}{100} > \frac{3}{4}$ **C** $\frac{7}{100} > 0.09$ **E** $0.65 < 0.09$

B $\frac{7}{100} > 0.65$ **D** $0.65 < \frac{3}{4}$

36. Mrs Breen has a grey top and a grey skirt, and a white top
and white skirt. She picks out a top at random and then a
skirt at random. Which of the following statements is correct?

A It's impossible to pick a white top and a white skirt.

B The probability of picking a white skirt is $\frac{1}{2}$.

C It's certain that she will pick either a grey top or a grey skirt.

D There is a higher probability of picking a grey top than a grey skirt.

E The probability of picking a white skirt is $\frac{1}{4}$.

37. Bill has a packing box that measures 10 cm × 8 cm × 8 cm.
He fills it with matchboxes that measure 2 cm × 2 cm × 1 cm.
How many matchboxes can he fit in the packing box?

Answer: _____

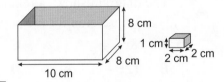

38. A barrel contains 4 litres of water. There are 5 holes in the bottom
of the barrel, and each hole loses 80 ml of water each hour.
How many hours will it take for the barrel to completely empty?

A 9 hours   **B** 10 hours   **C** 11 hours   **D** 12 hours   **E** 13 hours

39. Yohan joined two rectangles together to make this shape.
The perimeter of the shape is 21 metres. What is the length of X?

Answer: _____ m

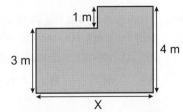

40. A sequence is described by the rule $3n^2 + 1$.
What are the first two terms in the sequence?

A 1, 3   **B** 4, 13   **C** 7, 13   **D** 10, 37   **E** 4, 7

/ 9

41. This flag is rotated 90° clockwise on the grid about the point (0, 0). What will be the new coordinates of point P?

Answer: (___ , ___)

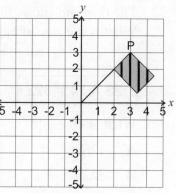

42. Mark has 3 cubes of cheese with sides of 2 cm. A mouse eats 12 cm³ of the cheese. What volume of cheese does Mark have left?

Answer: _____ cm³

43. Lemone is opening up a plant stall in the market. She buys the stall (S) and boxes of cactus plants (C) to sell. Each box contains 12 cactus plants and Lemone buys 60 cactus plants altogether. Which expression shows the total cost?

A $12SC$ **B** $S + 5C$ **C** $SC + 12$ **D** $5SC$ **E** $S + 60C$

44. The arrow on the spinner is pointing at number 1. Charlotte spins the arrow round 315° anti-clockwise. Which number is the arrow pointing at now?

Answer: _____

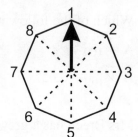

45. Which equation gives the nth term of this sequence?

     -1, -1, -1, -1, -1

A $2n - 3$ **C** $n^2 - n$ **E** $(n - 1)^2$

B $n - 1$ **D** $n - (n + 1)$

46. Duncan has £2.73. He has the same number of 2p and 1p coins, and these are the only coins that he has. How many 1p coins does he have?

Answer: _____

47. The diagram shows a regular pentagon. Which of the following is an expression for the perimeter of the pentagon?

A $8x - 4y$ **C** $5x - 5y$ **E** $2x + 5y$

B $(2x - y) + 5$ **D** $10x - 5y$

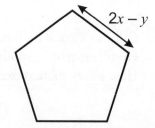

48. There are 22 children and 7 adults at a party. Sherrie cooks 3 sausage rolls for each child and 5 sausage rolls for each adult. If the sausage rolls come in packets of 25, how many packets will Sherrie need to buy?

Answer: _____

49. Moses is tiling his rectangular bathroom floor. Each tile is 0.04 m² and he uses 100 whole tiles to cover the entire floor. If the width of his bathroom is 1 m, what is the length of his bathroom?

A 2 m   **B** 4 m   **C** 7 m   **D** 5 m   **E** 6 m

50. Which of these expressions equals $3x + 18y$?

A $3(6xy)$ **C** $21x - 3y$ **E** $2x + x + 3y^2$

B $6(x + 3y)$ **D** $3(x + 6y)$

/ 10

Assessment Test 2

Assessment Test 3

Allow 50 minutes to do this test. Work as quickly and as carefully as you can.

You can print **multiple-choice answer sheets** for these questions from our website — go to www.cgplearning.co.uk/11+. If you'd prefer to answer them in standard write-in format, either write your answers in the spaces provided or circle the **correct answer** from the options **A** to **E**.

1. Each of the small squares in the shape on the right has an area of 1 cm².

    What is the total area of the shape?

    Answer: _____ cm²

    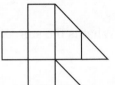

2. How many lines of symmetry does the hexagon on the right have?

    A 1   **B** 2   **C** 3   **D** 4   **E** 6

    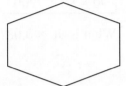

3. Which unit is most suitable for measuring the length of a football pitch?

    A   centimetres   **C**   metres   **E**   litres
    B   millimetres   **D**   kilometres

4. Elsa counts the vehicles that pass her school during her lunchtime. The pictogram shows her results.

    How many buses did she see?

    Answer: _____

Vehicle type	Number of vehicles
Car	
Van	= 4
Bus	
Taxi	

5. The Venn diagram on the right shows how many children in a class have bikes, skateboards and scooters.

    How many children have a skateboard and a scooter, but not a bike?

    Answer: _____

    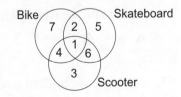

6. Maddy buys a tomato salad, some coleslaw and a jacket potato.

    How much change will she receive from a £5 note?

    A £1.64   **B** £2.16   **C** £3.36   **D** £33.60   **E** £3.63

Salad bar	
Coleslaw	25p
Green salad	80p
Tomato salad	40p
Rice salad	50p
Potato salad	45p
Jacket potato	99p
Rice	85p

7. Which of the following times is the same as 13:45?

    A 1:45 pm   **B** 2:45 am   **C** 1:45 am   **D** 3:45 pm   **E** 2:45 pm

8. Sasha starts her homework at 4:20 pm. She can stop and go to visit her friend when she has done 1¾ hours of homework.

    What time can she visit her friend?

    Answer: _____ pm

9. What is 9.45 ÷ 1.5 ?

    A 3.6   **B** 14.175   **C** 630   **D** 6.3   **E** 63

/ 9

Carry on to the next question → →

10. Which is the most likely mass of a tin of soup?

   A 0.4 g   **B** 400 g   **C** 40 kg   **D** 4 kg   **E** 4 g

11. This chart shows the number of boys and
   girls in each year group in a school.

   How many children are in the biggest year group?

   Answer: _____

Year Group	Boys	Girls
3	49	50
4	52	56
5	55	57
6	54	59
7	10	20

12. What is the sum of the numbers of faces, edges and vertices of a cube?

   Answer: _____

13. $90 \times 80 = 7200$

   What is 90×0.08?

   Answer: _____

14. 1.75 pints = 1 litre. How many pint bottles
   would you need to hold 6 litres of water?

   Answer: _____

15. Which of the shapes on the right has exactly
   one pair of parallel sides?

   Answer: _____

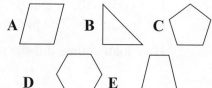

A   **B**   **C**   **D**   **E**

16. Ben makes this pattern by repeating three shapes over and over again.
   How many hearts will there be in the first 20 shapes?

   A 6   **B** 7   **C** 3   **D** 8   **E** 4

17. A group of children have a competition to see who is
   fastest at running from one end of the playground to the other.

   The results are shown in the table on the right.
   Who came second?

   Answer: _____

Name	Time
Betsy	4 mins 18 secs
Cara	3 mins 59 secs
Ian	4 mins 2 secs
Sian	4 mins 20 secs
Tony	4 mins 27 secs

18. Ian buys 6 sandwiches costing £1.99 each
   and 3 drinks costing 49p each.

   He does this calculation to estimate the cost: $6 \times £2 + 3 \times £0.50$
   How does his estimate differ from the exact cost?

   A   £12 too much   **C**   12p too little   **E**   6p too much
   B   9p too much   **D**   9p too little

19. $349 \times 84 = 29\,316$

   What is 349×42?

   A 7329   **B** 146 580   **C** 17 264   **D** 58 632   **E** 14 658

   / 10

   Carry on to the next question → →

20. What is the probability of throwing a number greater than 4 on a fair, six-sided dice.

A ⅙   **B** ⅚   **C** 4/6   **D** ⅓   **E** ⅔

21. Look at these fractions.

$$\frac{7}{20} \quad \frac{3}{4} \quad \frac{1}{5} \quad \frac{3}{20} \quad \frac{5}{20}$$

Which of the following shows them arranged from smallest to largest?

A 3/20, 1/5, 5/20, 3/4, 7/20

B 3/20, 1/5, 5/20, 7/20, 3/4

C 3/20, 3/4, 1/5, 5/20, 7/20

D 3/4, 7/20, 5/20, 1/5, 3/20

E 1/5, 3/20, 5/20, 7/20, 3/4

22. The temperature of a patient at 9 am each day was recorded and plotted on a graph.

What is the range of the temperatures?

Answer: _____ °C

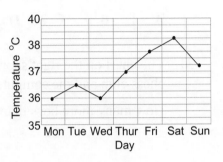

23. Sue's car uses 5 full tanks of petrol to travel 2985 miles. How many miles can she travel on one full tank of petrol?

Answer: _____ miles

24. Jenny is standing facing north at the point marked X on the grid.

She moves 3 units forward, then makes an anticlockwise turn through 135°. Which letter is she now facing?

Answer: _____

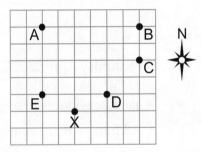

25. Which number should go in the circle to make this equation correct?

$$4 \times 56 + \bigcirc \times 56 = 560$$

Answer: _____

26. Which diagram on the right shows how this 3-dimensional shape would look when viewed from directly above?

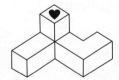

Answer: _____

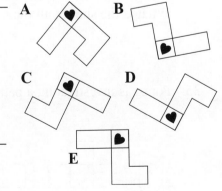

27. John thinks of a number. He multiplies it by 11 and subtracts 9. The answer he gets is 112.

What number did he start with?

Answer: _____

/ 8

Carry on to the next question → →

Assessment Test 3

28. This table shows the number of awards each class were given.
    What is the mean number of awards?

Class	6A	6B	6C	6D	6E	6F
Number of awards	16	16	11	17	12	12

Answer: _____

29. The diagram shows a garden with a flower bed.
    What is the area of the lawn?

Answer: _____ m²

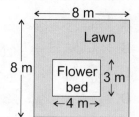

30. Luke started at –5 and counted up in steps of 1.5.
    Which of the following numbers did he count?

    A –1   **B** 0   **C** 2   **D** 3   **E** 4

31. The chart on the right shows the proportions of boys and girls in the
    chess club and the computer club. There are 30 children in each club.

    How many more boys than girls are there in the computer club?

    Answer: _____

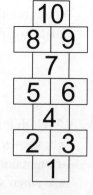

32. Sarah has run a total distance of 168 km over a 12 week period.
    How far does she run each day if she runs the same distance each day?

    Answer: _____ km

33. On Saturday April 23rd, Claire's father tells her that it is 6 weeks
    until they go on holiday. They are going on holiday on a Saturday.
    What date will this be?

    A 1st June   **B** 2nd June   **C** 3rd June   **D** 4th June   **E** 5th June

34. On the right is a hopscotch grid. The sum of the numbers on the grid is 55.

    The grid is extended so that the greatest number at the top of the grid is 20.
    What is the sum of all the numbers on the grid?

    Answer: _____

35. Poppy is investigating a pattern made of squares.

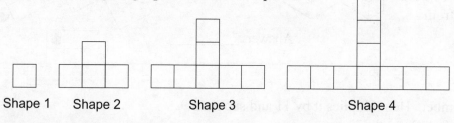

Shape 1   Shape 2   Shape 3   Shape 4

    How many squares will be in the shape 11 of the pattern?

    Answer: _____

/ 8

Carry on to the next question → →

Assessment Test 3

36. Caleb pours ⅖ of a litre of water out of a full 10 litre bucket.
    How many millilitres are left in the bucket?

    A 960 ml **B** 9600 ml **C** 96 ml **D** 6000 ml **E** 4000 ml

37. Which statement below is true about the spinner on the right?

    A It is equally likely to land on an odd or even number.
    B There is an even chance of it landing on a number greater than 4.
    C The probability of it landing on 2 is ⅛.
    D The probability of it landing on an even number is ⅓.
    E The probability of it landing on a number less than 3 is ½.

    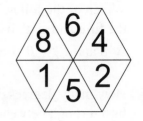

38. The diagram shows the coordinates of three corners
    of a rectangle.

    What are the coordinates of corner T?

    Answer: (_____,_____)

    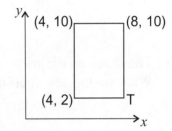

39. A school holds a concert. There are 42 rows of 48 seats.
    How many seats are there?

    Answer: _____

40. | Volume of a triangular prism = area of triangular side × length |

    What is the volume of this triangular prism?

    Answer: _____ cm³

    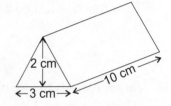

41. Which number is exactly half-way between 4.19 and 3.81?

    A 4.1 **B** 4 **C** 3.9 **D** 3.09 **E** 4.09

42. The perimeter of a rectangular floor tile is 128 cm.
    The tile is three times as long as it is wide. What is its length?

    Answer: _____ cm

43. Sleeping bags are given a rating to show the minimum
    temperature they can be used at:

Sleeping bag rating	1	2	3	4	5
Minimum temperature (°C)	5	0	−5	−10	−15

    Adam needs to buy a sleeping bag that he can use at 25 °F.
    The graph on the right can be used to change a temperature in °F
    to a temperature in °C.

    What is the lowest rating of sleeping bag can buy?

    Answer: _____

    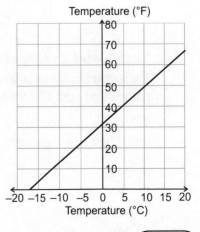

    / 8

Carry on to the next question → →

Assessment Test 3

44. The ages in months of four out of the six babies at a clinic are given below.

6	3	8	2

The median age of the 6 babies is 4.5 months.
The median age of these four babies is also 4.5 months.
Which of the following could be the ages in months of
the fifth and sixth babies?

A 8 and 12   B 1 and 2   C 2 and 8   D 11 and 12   E 3 and 4

45. How many degrees does the minute hand on a clock
turn through between 12 noon and 10:30 pm?

A 3160°   B 3780°   C 2300°   D 2430°   E 3600°

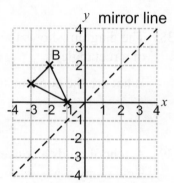

46. The shape on the grid is reflected in the mirror line.
What are the new coordinates of point B?

Answer: (____,____)

47. A printer uses the following formula to work out
the cost, C, in pounds, of printing m leaflets:

$$C = 15(m \div 100) + 5.$$

How much will it cost to have 300 leaflets printed?

Answer: £_____

48. James records the weather for 20 days. He draws a pie chart of his results.
It was foggy for 3 days. What size angle should he draw to represent this?

A 90°   B 54°   C 36°   D 45°   E 180°

49. Rashid gets £2.50 pocket money each week. He is given
an extra 30% pocket money if he cleans the family car.

How much money will he receive over 3 weeks
if he cleans the car each week?

Answer: £_____

50. Russell wins £500 in a prize draw.
He spends £260 on a new computer, and decides to buy some
games that cost £39.99 each.

Which expression gives the amount of money Russell will have
left if he buys n games?

A 240n

B 500 – 260n

C 240 + 39.99n

D 240 – 39.99n

E 500 – 39.99n

/7

Assessment Test 4

Allow 50 minutes to do this test. Work as quickly and as carefully as you can.

You can print **multiple-choice answer sheets** for these questions from our website — go to www.cgplearning.co.uk/11+. If you'd prefer to answer them in standard write-in format, either write your answers in the spaces provided or circle the **correct answer** from the options **A** to **E**.

1. What is the value of the 7 in 7 230 000?

    A   seven hundred million   **D**   seventy million
    B   seven hundred thousand   **E**   seven million
    C   seventy thousand

2. Which of the following is most likely to be the height of a fully grown tree?

    A   12 metres   **C**   1.2 centimetres   **E**   0.12 metres
    B   12 millimetres   **D**   0.12 centimetres

3. Tallulah has drawn a trapezium.

    She reflects her shape in the dotted mirror line shown to make a new shape. What type of shape does she form?

    A   pentagon   **C**   heptagon   **E**   quadrilateral
    B   octagon   **D**   hexagon

4. Courtney records the temperature each day for five days.

    On which day does she record the lowest temperature?

Day	Monday	Tuesday	Wednesday	Thursday	Friday
Temperature	−2 °C	1 °C	0 °C	2 °C	−1 °C

    Answer: _____

5. Ted's favourite TV programme is shown in the evening. It starts and finishes at the times shown on the clocks.

    How long does the programme last for?

    Answer: _____ hour(s) _____ mins

    Start   Finish

6. What is the area of this shape?

    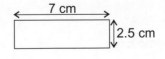

    Answer: _____ cm²

7. Which of these numbers is smallest?

    0.81   1.92   12.4   21.42   0.18

    Answer: _____

    / 7

Carry on to the next question →→

Assessment Test 4

8. Jane and Sue are playing a game. Jane starts at point (4, 3).
   She moves 1 unit east and 2 units south on the grid.
   Which point (A, B, C, D or E) does she end up at?

   Answer: _____

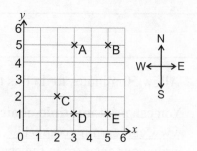

9. Lucas lives in Kneesall.
   He needs to be at his school in
   Rippen by 8.40 am to go on a trip.

   The timetable shows the bus times.

Bus depot	8:00 am	8:05 am	8:10 am	8:15 am	8:20 am
Kneesall	8:10 am	8:15 am	8:20 am	8:25 am	8:30 am
Rippen	8:15 am	8:20 am	8:25 am	8:30 am	8:35 am
Hathern	8:29 am	8:34 am	8:39 am	8:44 am	8:49 am

   What is the latest time he can catch a bus?

   Answer: _____ am

10. The frequency chart shows the results of throwing a dice.
    How many times was the dice thrown altogether?

    Answer: _____

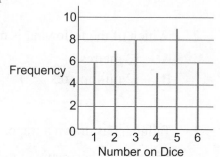

11. Macy buys four bunches of flowers.
    One of the bunches costs £1.99.
    The other three bunches cost £1.49 each.

    What is the total cost of the flowers?

    A £6.59   **B** £6.46   **C** £5.56   **D** £5.64   **E** £64.60

12. Estimate the size of angle x.
    A 10°   **B** 95°   **C** 80°   **D** 15°   **E** 45°

13. How much does the kitten on the right weigh?

    A   2.5 kg   **C**   2.25 kg   **E**   2.25 g
    B   2.05 g   **D**   0.5 kg

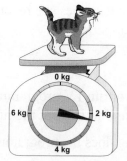

14. A regular heptagon has a perimeter of 56 cm.
    How long is each side?

    Answer: _____ cm

15. This chart shows the masses of some bags
    of fruit on sale in a supermarket.

    Mr Smith buys 1 bag of oranges, 2 bags of bananas,
    3 bags of apples and 1 bag of pears.

    How many kilograms of fruit has he bought?

Fruit	Mass per bag (g)
Oranges	600
Bananas	450
Apples	500
Pears	750

    Answer: _____ kg

    / 8

Carry on to the next question →→

16. Joe eats three loaves of bread on a seven day holiday.
    He eats the same amount of bread each day.
    What fraction of a loaf does he eat each day of the holiday?

    A $\frac{1}{7}$ **B** $\frac{3}{7}$ **C** $\frac{1}{4}$ **D** $\frac{4}{7}$ **E** $\frac{1}{3}$

17. This pie chart shows the pets belonging to the children in Sue's class.
    The total number of pets in the survey is 32.

    Which of the following is the best estimate for
    the number of dogs owned by the class?

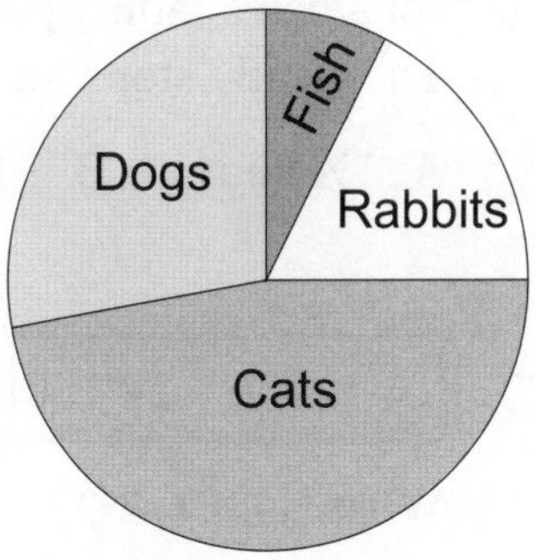

    A 8   **B** 15   **C** 18   **D** 6   **E** 9

18. Li estimates the answer to 39×43 by rounding both numbers to
    the nearest 10 before multiplying them. What answer should he get?

    A 1500   **B** 1600   **C** 1200   **D** 2000   **E** 1677

19. Harriet's class is split into groups. There are 4 boys and
    3 girls in each group. There are 15 girls in the class.
    How many children are in her class?

    Answer: _____

20. Tammy is buying some cakes for her birthday party.
    Which of the following is the cheapest price per cake?

    A 15p each   **C** 10 for £1   **E** 15 for £1.50
    B 3 for 39p   **D** 25 for £2

21. A caterer is making a sauce. She uses 2.25 kg of apples for every 1 kg of sugar.
    How many kilograms of apples will she need if she uses 9 kg of sugar?

    A 4 kg   **B** 202.5 kg   **C** 2.025 kg   **D** 2025 kg   **E** 20.25 kg

22. Look at the information on the right for a breakfast cereal.
    How much carbohydrate would be in a 20 gram serving of cereal?

    Answer: _____ g

A 30 gram serving contains:

Protein	4 g
Carbohydrate	21 g
Fat	1.5 g
Fibre	0.8 g
Salt	0.5 g

23. A piece of ribbon is 48 m long.
    It is cut into pieces that are each $\frac{1}{3}$ m long.
    How many pieces are there?

    Answer: _____

24. Rashid is thinking of a 3D shape.
    The shape has 4 faces, 4 vertices and 6 edges.
    Which of the following could Rashid's shape be?

    A   square-based pyramid   **D**   cylinder
    B   triangle-based pyramid   **E**   cube
    C   triangular prism

/ 9

Carry on to the next question → →

Assessment Test 4

25. Kate buys a second-hand car for £3,080. The original cost of the car was £6,999. By how much has the car's value decreased?

Answer: £ _____

26. Jonathan's family go on a journey which is shown on this graph. The family stops for a break. How long does the break last for?

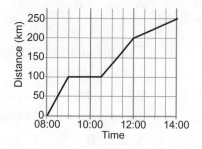

A 1½ hours **B** 1 hour **C** 2 hours **D** ½ hour **E** 1¾ hours

27.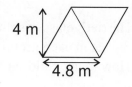

$30 \times 806 = 24\ 180$

What is 30×403?

A 1209 **B** 12 900 **C** 48 360 **D** 4836 **E** 12 090

28. The diagram shows a patio made from two identical triangular slabs. What is the area of the patio?

A 3.84 m² **C** 480 m² **E** 192 m²

B 19.2 m² **D** 38.4 m²

29. A school buys some badges to sell at the summer fair. The school pays 70p for each badge and sells them for £1 each.

The school sells all the badges, and makes a profit of £60. How many badges did the school buy?

Answer: _____

30. Fred asked all the children in Year 6 what their favourite crisp flavour was. The bar chart shows his results.

Which two flavours together were as popular as Ready Salted?

Answer: _____ and _____

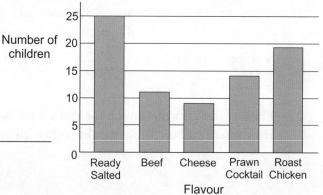

31. Look at the volumes shown below. Find the total volume.

5.555 litres   5.55 litres   5.5 litres   5.0 litres   0.5 litres   Answer: _____ litres

32. Class 7 have made 250 biscuits to sell at the school fair. They pack them in bags of 12.

How many biscuits are left over?

Answer: _____

33. A bag contains 5 cherry sweets and 10 lime sweets. What is the probability of randomly picking a cherry sweet?

A ⁵⁄₁₀ **B** ¹⁰⁄₁₅ **C** ⅓ **D** ½ **E** ¾

/ 9

Carry on to the next question →→

34. Find the sum of all the square numbers between 46 and 91.

Answer: _____

35. The pictogram shows the number of awards
Class 7 gained each day in a week.

What is the modal number of awards?

Answer: _____

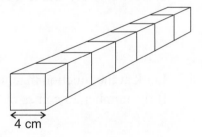

Mon ⬤⬤⬤⬤⬤
Tue ⬤⬤⬤⬤◖
Wed ⬤⬤⬤   ⬤ = 3 awards
Thur ⬤⬤⬤◖
Fri ⬤⬤◖

36. A bag contains some striped and spotted balls.
The pattern on the balls is either red or yellow.
The sorting diagram shows how many of each ball there are.

Which type of ball is most likely to be pulled out at random?

	spotted	striped
yellow	6	3
red	4	7

A a red ball   **C** a striped ball   **E** a red striped ball
B a yellow ball   **D** a spotted ball

37. The table shows how much Ahmed saves each month.

What is Ahmed's mean monthly saving for these 6 months?

Answer: £ _____

January	£1.20
February	80p
March	£1.50
April	£1.10
May	£1.50
June	50p

38. Mark takes seven 4 cm cubes and places them end to end
to make this shape.

He then puts the shape on a piece of paper, and draws
around it with a pencil.

What is the perimeter of the shape that he draws?

Answer: _____ cm

4 cm

39. Simon is investigating patterns made from triangles.
Which formula represents the number of small triangles
in the nth pattern in the series?

A $n + 1$ **B** $n^2 + 1$ **C** n **D** n^2 **E** $n^2 - 1$

Pattern 1   Pattern 2   Pattern 3

Pattern 4   Pattern 5

40. A dog eats 245 g of dried food per meal.
She has 3 meals per day.

How much food does the dog eat in a week?

A 0.4725 kg   **C** 3.375 kg   **E** 47.25 kg
B 5.145 kg   **D** 1.575 kg

41. The table shows the opening times of a café.
The cost of running the café is £10 per hour.

How much more per week does it cost to run
the café in the summer than in the winter?

Answer: £ _____

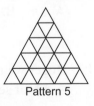

	Opens	Closes
Mar – Sep	9 am	6 pm
Oct – Feb	11 am	4 pm

/ 8

Carry on to the next question → →

Assessment Test 4

42. The net folds up to form a 3-dimensional shape.
What is the volume of this shape?

Answer: _____ cm³

43. Katie buys six 1 litre cartons of milk each week.
She drinks 350 ml of milk twice a day.
She uses the whole carton before she opens a new one.
How much milk will be left over after 7 days?

Answer: _____ ml

44. Oscar faces north and then turns through 225° in a clockwise direction.
Which direction is he now facing?

A west   B south west   C south east   D south   E east

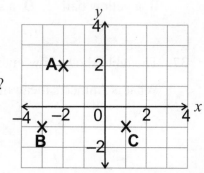

45. Bilal is drawing a parallelogram on a coordinate grid.
Points A, B and C are three of the corners of the parallelogram.

What are the coordinates of the fourth corner of the parallelogram?

Answer: (___ , ___)

46. $x^2 - 1 > 49$

If x is a positive whole number, what is the smallest it could be?

Answer: _____

47. Look at the function machine on the right.
If the number 25 comes out of the machine what number went in?

? —(× 5)—(÷ 7)—→ 25

Answer: _____

48. Which formula can be used to work out the nth term of this series?

    −1   1   3   5   7

A $3n$ B $n - 3$ C $2n - 3$ D $2 \div n - 3$ E $2n + 3$

49. Roger wants to spread grass seed on a rectangular area of soil.
A tub of seed costs £5.99 and covers 12 square metres of soil.

How much will the seed cost altogether if Roger's area of soil
measures 8 metres by 6 metres?

Answer: £_____

50. Lucy wants to buy a T-shirt in a sale.
All items in the sale are reduced by 60%.

What is the sale price of the T-shirt if the original price was £n?

A $n \div 60$ B $\frac{2}{5}(n)$ C $n - 60$ D $\frac{3}{5}(n)$ E $2n - 6$

/ 9

M6OF1

Page 6

To find the rule in a sequence, find how to get from one number to another. It can help to look at the difference between the numbers, or try to spot a pattern, e.g. the numbers double each time.

1. 21
The rule of the sequence is add 3.
So the missing term = 18 + 3 = 21.

2. 101
The rule of the sequence is subtract 3.
So the missing term = 104 – 3 = 101.

3. 16
The rule of the sequence is subtract 5.
So the missing term = 21 – 5 = 16.

4. 2
The rule of the sequence is add 0.25.
So the missing term = 1.75 + 0.25 = 2.

5. 4
The rule of the sequence is double the previous number.
So the missing term must be half of the following term, 8 ÷ 2 = 4.

6. 22
The sequence is 6, 10, 14, 18, 22...

7. 10
The sequence is 30, 25, 20, 15, 10...

8. 48
The sequence is 3, 6, 12, 24, 48...

9. 3
The sequence is 19, 15, 11, 7, 3...

10. 7
The sequence is 5, 5½, 6, 6½, 7...

11. 21
There are 6 sticks in the first shape, 11 in the second shape, and 16 in the third shape. So each shape has 5 sticks more than the shape before. The next shape will be made of 16 + 5 = 21 sticks.

12. 22
There are 4 sticks in the first shape, 10 in the second shape, and 16 in the third shape. So each shape has 6 sticks more than the shape before. The next shape will be made of 16 + 6 = 22 sticks.

13. 10
Continuing the sequence, 20 – 15 = 5, so 5 is the sixth number. The seventh number is the difference between the 5th and the 6th numbers. 15 – 5 = 10. 10 is the seventh number.

14. 37
Tom's sequence is 73, 64, 55, 46, 37...
Mark's sequence is 25, 29, 33, 37...

15. -0.25
Nadiah's sequence is: 6, 4.75, 3.5, 2.25, 1, -0.25.

Page 7

To find a fraction of a number, divide the number by the denominator and multiply the result by the numerator.

1. 6
$\frac{1}{2}$ of 12, 12 ÷ 2 = 6, 6 × 1 = 6

2. 3
$\frac{1}{3}$ of 9, 9 ÷ 3 = 3, 3 × 1 = 3

3. 2
$\frac{2}{8}$ of 8, 8 ÷ 8 = 1, 1 × 2 = 2

4. 8
$\frac{2}{6}$ of 24, 24 ÷ 6 = 4, 4 × 2 = 8

5. 27
$\frac{3}{4}$ of 36, 36 ÷ 4 = 9, 9 × 3 = 27

6. $\frac{1}{3}$ of 27
$\frac{1}{4}$ of 32. 32 ÷ 4 = 8, 8 × 1 = 8
$\frac{1}{3}$ of 27. 27 ÷ 3 = 9, 9 × 1 = 9

7. $\frac{2}{3}$ of 33
$\frac{2}{3}$ of 33. 33 ÷ 3 = 11, 11 × 2 = 22
$\frac{1}{5}$ of 100. 100 ÷ 5 = 20, 20 × 1 = 20

8. $\frac{2}{5}$ of 25
$\frac{2}{5}$ of 25. 25 ÷ 5 = 5, 5 × 2 = 10
$\frac{1}{2}$ of 18. 18 ÷ 2 = 9, 9 × 1 = 9

9. $\frac{4}{5}$ of 35
$\frac{4}{5}$ of 35. 35 ÷ 5 = 7, 7 × 4 = 28
$\frac{5}{6}$ of 30. 30 ÷ 6 = 5, 5 × 5 = 25

10. $\frac{7}{8}$ of 48
$\frac{1}{3}$ of 120. 120 ÷ 3 = 40, 40 × 1 = 40
$\frac{7}{8}$ of 48. 48 ÷ 8 = 6, 6 × 7 = 42

11. $\frac{2}{3}$
8 apples divided between 12 children would give $\frac{8}{12}$ of an apple for each child. This fraction can be simplified to $\frac{2}{3}$ if you divide the numerator and the denominator by 4.

12. $\frac{3}{8}$
6 out of the 16 squares are shaded, giving the fraction . This can be simplified to $\frac{3}{8}$ if you divide the numerator and the denominator by 2.

13. 33
There are six sixths in 1 ($\frac{6}{6}$ = 1), so in 5 there are 30 sixths (6 × 5). If there are six sixths in 1, then in $\frac{1}{2}$ there will be three sixths. 30 + 3 = 33.

14. 20
Martha had 12 marbles after giving $\frac{2}{5}$ to Joseph, so 12 is $\frac{3}{5}$ of the total number of marbles. If $\frac{3}{5}$ = 12, then $\frac{1}{5}$ = 12 ÷ 3 = 4. So the total number of marbles she started with = 4 × 5 = 20

15. 20p
Dog Empire — 2 chews would cost 1 + 50p = £1.50. So 4 chews would cost £1.50 + £1.50 = £3. Dog Shop — Before a discount, 4 chews would cost 4 × £1.20 = £4.80. As Aarti is buying at least 3, she gets $\frac{1}{3}$ off. $\frac{1}{3}$ of £4.80 is £4.80 ÷ 3 = £1.60.
So the price of 4 chews is £4.80 – £1.60 = £3.20.
The difference in price is £3.20 – £3 = 20p

Page 8

1. $\frac{29}{100}$
29% means '29 out of 100'.

2. 0.15
To convert a percentage into a decimal, divide it by 100.
15% ÷ 100 = 0.15

3.   62%

$^{31}/_{50}$ is equivalent to $^{62}/_{100}$ if you multiply the numerator and the denominator by 2. $^{62}/_{100}$ is 62%.

4. $^{23}/_{50}$

46% means '46 out of 100'. So that's $^{46}/_{100}$.
This can be simplified to $^{23}/_{50}$ by dividing the numerator and the denominator by 2.

5.   0.03

$^{3}/_{100}$ means $3 \div 100 = 0.03$

6.   7

To find 10% of 70 you can divide 70 by 100 and multiply the result by 10. This is the same as just dividing 70 by 10, so 10% of 70 is $70 \div 10 = 7$

7.   3

25% of 12 is the same as $^{1}/_{4}$ of 12. $12 \div 4 = 3, 3 \times 1 = 3$

8.   36

75% of 48 is the same as $^{3}/_{4}$ of 48. $48 \div 4 = 12, 12 \times 3 = 36$

9.   128

1% of 6400 is $6400 \div 100 = 64$, 2% is $64 \times 2 = 128$

10.   24

To find 10% of 80 you can divide 80 by 100 and multiply the result by 10. This is the same as dividing 80 by 10, so 10% of 80 is $80 \div 10 = 8$, 30% will be $8 \times 3 = 24$

11.   60%

There are five triangles, so each triangle is $100 \div 5 = 20\%$ of the shape. Three triangles are not shaded, so this is $3 \times 20\% = 60\%$ of the shape.

Alternatively, 3 out of the 5 triangles aren't shaded, so that's $^{3}/_{5}$. This is equivalent to $^{60}/_{100}$ (multiply the numerator and the denominator by 20). $^{60}/_{100} = 60\%$.

12.   £8.40

10% of £10.50 is £10.50 $\div$ 10 = £1.05.
So, 20% = £1.05 $\times$ 2 = £2.10
£10.50 – £2.10 = £8.40

13.   13

Find the total of red and yellow roses. 40% are red.
10% is $30 \div 10 = 3$. So 40% = $4 \times 3 = 12$ red roses.
$^{1}/_{6}$ are yellow. $30 \div 6 = 5$, So, $5 \times 1 = 5$ yellow roses.
So $30 - 12 - 5 = 13$ white roses.

14.   40%

Add up the total number of pupils.
$10 + 4 + 12 + 4 = 30$. 12 out of 30 take the bus, so $^{12}/_{30}$ — you can simplify this to $^{4}/_{10}$ by dividing the numerator and the denominator by 3. $^{4}/_{10}$ is equivalent to $^{40}/_{100}$ — so that's 40%.

15.   75% of 40

25% of 88. 25% is $^{1}/_{4}$, so, $88 \div 4 = 22$
$^{2}/_{3}$ of 36. $36 \div 3 = 12, 12 \times 2 = 24$
$^{4}/_{5}$ of 30. $30 \div 5 = 6, 6 \times 4 = 24$
20% of 80. 10% is $80 \div 10 = 8$. So, 20% = $8 \times 2 = 16$
75% of 40. 75% is $^{3}/_{4}$, so, $40 \div 4 = 10, 10 \times 3 = 30$

Section Two — Working with Numbers

Page 9

There are different methods that you can use for addition. The partitioning method has been used for questions 1-9 below. It involves breaking up one number into units, tens, hundreds, etc. and adding each of the parts to the other number, one at a time. It's usually easier to partition the smaller of the two numbers you're adding. Alternatively, you could use the column method for these questions.

1.   128

56 breaks into $50 + 6$. $72 + 50 = 122, 122 + 6 = 128$

2.   393

135 breaks into $100 + 30 + 5$.
$258 + 100 = 358, 358 + 30 = 388$,
$388 + 5 = 393$

3.   1213

268 breaks into $200 + 60 + 8$.
$945 + 200 = 1145$
$1145 + 60 = 1205$
$1205 + 8 = 1213$

4.   2253

1076 breaks into $1000 + 70 + 6$.
$1177 + 1000 = 2177$
$2177 + 70 = 2247$
$2247 + 6 = 2253$

5.   8171

3303 breaks into $3000 + 300 + 3$.
$4868 + 3000 = 7868$
$7868 + 300 = 8168$
$8168 + 3 = 8171$

6.   24

6.2 breaks into $6 + 0.2$.
$17.8 + 6 = 23.8, 23.8 + 0.2 = 24$

7.   12.8

3.5 breaks into $3 + 0.5$. $9.3 + 3 = 12.3, 12.3 + 0.5 = 12.8$

8.   15.81

4.58 breaks into $4 + 0.5 + 0.08$
$11.23 + 4 = 15.23$
$15.23 + 0.5 = 15.73$
$15.73 + 0.08 = 15.81$

9.   50.2

24.5 breaks into $20 + 4 + 0.5$.
$25.7 + 20 = 45.7$
$45.7 + 4 = 49.7$
$49.7 + 0.5 = 50.2$

10.   56.96

Both numbers have four digits here, so it's probably easier to use the column method.

```
  3 4 . 2 3
+ 2 2 . 7 3
-----------
  5 6 . 9 6
```

It's often easiest to add several numbers using the column method:

11. **£1.63**

$$
\begin{array}{r}
3\,8 \\
6\,4 \\
3\,2 \\
+\quad 2\,9 \\
\hline
1\,6\,3 \\
1\,2
\end{array}
$$

The amounts were all in pence, so the total is 163p. 163p is the same as £1.63

12. **18.6 cm**

$$
\begin{array}{r}
4\,.\,0 \\
2\,.\,0 \\
3\,.\,5 \\
4\,.\,4 \\
+\quad 4\,.\,7 \\
\hline
1\,8\,.\,6 \\
1\,1
\end{array}
$$

13. **£673.60**

$$
\begin{array}{r}
4\,9\,0\,.\,9\,0 \\
5\,5\,.\,5\,0 \\
+1\,2\,7\,.\,2\,0 \\
\hline
6\,7\,3\,.\,6\,0 \\
1\,1\,1
\end{array}
$$

14. **D**

A bacon roll, toast and jam, and coffee comes to £3.55.

$$
\begin{array}{r}
1\,.\,4\,5 \\
1\,.\,2\,5 \\
+\quad .\,8\,5 \\
\hline
3\,.\,5\,5 \\
1\ \ 1
\end{array}
$$

15. **52.35 kg**

Add up the weights of the four parcels (remember to line up the decimal places correctly).

$$
\begin{array}{r}
2\,4\,.\,5 \\
1\,6\,.\,2 \\
6\,.\,2\,5 \\
+\quad 5\,.\,4 \\
\hline
5\,2\,.\,3\,5 \\
2\ 1
\end{array}
$$

Page 10

You could use partitioning to find the answers to these subtractions. Break up the smaller number into units, tens, hundreds, etc. and subtract each of the parts from the other number, one at a time. Alternatively, you could use the column method.

1. **24**
32 breaks into 30 + 2. 56 – 30 = 26, 26 – 2 = 24

2. **55**
29 breaks into 20 + 9. 84 – 20 = 64, 64 – 9 = 55

3. **704**
358 breaks into 300 + 50 + 8. 1062 – 300 = 762,
762 – 50 = 712, 712 – 8 = 704.

4. **181.8**
82.5 breaks into 80 + 2 + 0.5
264.3 – 80 = 184.3
184.3 – 2 = 182.3
182.3 – 0.5 = 181.8

5. **9.04**
4.16 breaks into 4 + 0.1 + 0.06.
13.2 – 4 = 9.2, 9.2 – 0.1 = 9.1, 9.1 – 0.06 = 9.04.

In questions 6-10, you're told the result of the subtraction, and you have to work out the number that was subtracted. You do this by subtracting the result from the bigger number.

6. **11**
31 breaks into 30 + 1. 42 – 30 = 12, 12 – 1 = 11.

7. **3.2**
2.1 breaks into 2 + 0.1
5.3 – 2 = 3.3, 3.3 – 0.1 = 3.2

8. **72**
52 breaks into 50 + 2. 124 – 50 = 74, 74 – 2 = 72

9. **7.6**
9.8 breaks into 9 + 0.8. 17.4 – 9 = 8.4, 8.4 – 0.8 = 7.6

10. **258**
406 breaks into 400 + 6.
664 – 400 = 264, 264 – 6 = 258

11. **6**
48 – 12 = 36, 36 – 15 = 21
21 – 6 = 15, 15 – 9 = 6. 6 were decorated with coffee icing.

12. **11**
Subtract the number of children getting off the bus at each point to keep track of how many are still on the bus. There were 60 children at the start.
60 – 15 = 45,
45 – 7 = 38,
38 – 4 = 34,
34 – 9 = 25,
25 – 14 = 11
There were 11 children on the bus when it reached Church Avenue. They all must get off there.

13. **71 cm**
Subtract each amount cut off from 320 cm:
320 cm – 120 cm = 200 cm,
200 cm – 63 cm = 137 cm,
137 cm – 66 cm = 71 cm.

14. **13p**
Add up the amounts that Rona and Jenny each spent:
Rona: £2.60 + £1.22 = £3.82
Jenny: £3.20 + 75p = £3.95
Now subtract the amount Rona spent from the amount Jenny spent: £3.95 – £3.82 = 13p.

15. **£5.56**
Use a rounding method for this question. £26.99 rounds to £27 (+ 1p). £6.99 rounds to £7 (+ 1p) and £2.46 rounds to £2.50 (+ 4p). 42 – 27 – 7 – 2.50 = £5.50.
You added a total of 6p extra when rounding so the amount of change = £5.50 + £0.06 = £5.56.

Page 11

When you multiply by 10, move the digits one place to the left. Move the digits two places to the left when you multiply by 100, and three places to the left when you multiply by 1000. (Use zero to fill any places to the left of the decimal point which are left empty.) When you're dividing by 10, 100 and 1000, you move the digits the same number of places, but to the right.

1. **1200**
Move 12 two places to the left.

2. 3600

Move 3.6 three places to the left.

3. 2.4

Move 0.24 one place to the left.

4. 16945.4

Move 169.454 two places to the left.

5. 62

Move 0.062 three places to the left.

6. 34.72

Move 3472 two places to the right.

7. 9.46

Move 94.6 one place to the right.

8. 0.483

Move 48.3 two places to the right.

9. 0.046

Move 0.46 one place to the right.

10. 3.205

Move 3205 three places to the right.

11. B

Division is the inverse operation of multiplication, so the missing number = 4720 ÷ 100. Moving the digits in 4720 two places to the right gives 47.2

12. 22.24 cm

2224 ÷ 100. Move 2224 two places to the right: 22.24 cm.

13. £2700

£2.70 = 1 pack. In a box there are 100 packs, so that will cost £2.70 × 100 = £270. Mrs Chapman buys 10 boxes, so that will cost £270 × 10 = £2700.

14. × 10 000

Kailash multiplies a number by 100, then he divides it by 10. This is the same as just multiplying by 10. (The number he has now is 10 times bigger than the one he started with.) Finally, he multiplies this number by 1000. Multiplying by 10, then by 1000 is the same as multiplying by 10 × 1000 = 10 000.

15. 26 300

Ampney's population is 2630. Bentley's population is 10 times smaller than Ampney, 2630 ÷ 10 = 263. Clifton's population is 1000 times larger than Bentley's, 263 × 1000 = 263 000. Dannett's population is 10 times smaller than Clifton's, 263 000 ÷ 10 = 26 300.

Pages 12-13

You could use partitioning to find the answer. Break up one number into units, tens, hundreds, etc. and multiply each of the parts with the other number, one at a time — then add them together. Or you could set the numbers out in columns and multiply them.

1. 104

*13 breaks into 10 + 3. 10 × 8 = 80
3 × 8 = 24, 80 + 24 = 104*

2. 216

*24 breaks into 20 + 4. 20 × 9 = 180
4 × 9 = 36, 180 + 36 = 216*

3. 238

It's often easier to use columns when multiplying two 2-digit numbers:

```
      1 7
  ×   1 4
    ‾‾‾‾‾‾
      6 8    (17 × 4)
       2
  + 1 7 0    (17 × 10)
    ‾‾‾‾‾‾
    2 3 8
       1
```

4. 1650

*330 breaks into 300 + 30.
300 × 5 = 1500, 30 × 5 = 150
1500 + 150 = 1650*

5. 1430

It's often easier to use columns when multiplying two 2-digit numbers:

```
      6 5
  ×   2 2
    ‾‾‾‾‾‾
    1 3 0    (65 × 2)
       1
  + 1 3 0 0    (65 × 20)
       1
    ‾‾‾‾‾‾
    1 4 3 0
```

6. 21.6

*3.6 breaks into 3 + 0.6. 6 × 3 = 18
6 × 0.6 = 3.6, 18 + 3.6 = 21.6*

7. 29.4

*4.2 breaks into 4 + 0.2. 7 × 4 = 28
7 × 0.2 = 1.4, 28 + 1.4 = 29.4*

8. 74.4

*9.3 breaks into 9 + 0.3. 8 × 9 = 72
8 × 0.3 = 2.4, 72 + 2.4 = 74.4*

9. 448

*6.4 breaks into 6 + 0.4. 70 × 6 = 420,
70 × 0.4 = 28, 420 + 28 = 448.*

10. 1.15

*0.23 breaks into 0.2 + 0.03.
5 × 0.2 = 1, 5 × 0.03 = 0.15
1 + 0.15 = 1.15*

11. £7.80

*Round £1.95 to £2, by adding 5p.
4 × 2 = 8, then minus the 20p (4 × 5p) you added to round the cost of the tickets. £8 – 20p = £7.80*

12. 84p

*2 bags cost 24p, so 1 bag would cost
24p ÷ 2 = 12p. 12p × 7 = 84p.*

13. 550 g

*The ingredients shown are for 8 pancakes, so to make 40 pancakes you need to multiply each amount by 5 (8 × 5 = 40). The amount of flour needed is 110 × 5, 110 breaks into 100 + 10.
100 × 5 = 500, 10 × 5 = 50
500 + 50 = 550 g*

14. 168.48

To get from 3.24 to 32.4 you multiply by 10. To get from 52 to 5.2 you divide by 10. So, the answer to 32.4 × 5.2 is the same as 3.24 × 52, which is 168.48.

15. D

Use estimation to solve this equation. 7.7 rounds up to 8 and 6.4 rounds down to 6. 8 × 6 = 48. The closest answer to this is Option D, 49.28.

16. 50 384

188 is double 94, so the answer will be double 25 192.

```
    2 5 1 9 2
  ×         2
    5 0 3 8 4
    1   1
```

17. C

Use your knowledge of place value and multiplication to estimate the value of the different calculations.
A: 52.7 can be rounded down to 50. It's being multiplied by eight tenths (0.8), so the answer will be around eight tenths of 50, which is 40 (50 ÷ 10 = 5. 5 × 8 = 40).
B: 0.527 is roughly one half (0.5). So the result of the calculation will be about half of 80 (around 40).
C: 5.27 can be rounded down to 5. The value of the calculation is around 5 × 800 = 4000.
D: 527 can be rounded down to 500. It's being multiplied by eight tenths (0.8), so the answer will be around eight tenths of 500, which is 400 (500 ÷ 10 = 50. 50 × 8 = 400).
E: 5270 can be rounded down to 5000. It's being multiplied by eight thousandths (0.008), so the answer will be around eight thousandths of 5000, which is 40 (5000 ÷ 1000 = 5. 5 × 8 = 40). C has the largest value (around 4000).

18. E

Option A is based on the fact that 8 is one quarter of 32, so the answer must be one quarter of 7712, or 7712 ÷ 4.
Option B is based on the fact that 64 is double 32, so the answer must be double 7712, or 7712 × 2.
Option C is based on the fact that 16 is half of 32, so the answer must be half of 7712, or 7712 ÷ 2.
Option D is based on the fact that 241 × 33 will be one lot of 241 more than 7712, so 7712 + 241 = 7953.
Option E is based on the fact that 4 is one eighth of 32. The equation should be 7712 ÷ 8 not 7712 ÷ 16. E is incorrect.

19. 286

Dave has 7 times as many stickers as Betty, so Dave has 7 × 26 = 182. Lorna has 3 times as many stickers as Betty, so Lorna has 3 × 26 = 78 stickers. 26 + 182 + 78 = 286 stickers.

20. C

Work each calculation out by ignoring the zeros, and multiplying the digits at the beginning of each number. Finally, put the same number of zeros that you ignored on the end of the answer.
A: 6 × 4000: 6 × 4 = 24. Three zeros have been ignored, so 6 × 4000 = 24 000
B: 70 × 300: 7 × 3 = 21. Three zeros have been ignored, so 70 × 300 = 21 000
C: 200 × 200: 2 × 2 = 4. Four zeros have been ignored, so 200 × 200 = 40 000.
D: 900 × 10: 9 × 1 = 9. Three zeros have been ignored, so 900 × 10 = 9000
E: 8 × 500: 8 × 5 = 40. Two zeros have been ignored, so 8 × 500 = 4000
C is the biggest calculation.

21. B

You can tell which calculation has the smallest value here just by looking at the numbers. 2.41 is the smallest left hand number in any of the calculations, and 0.06 is the smallest right hand number in any of the calculations. Therefore, 2.41 × 0.06 (B) has the smallest value.

22. E

Estimate the answer to each option.
A: 50 × 250 = 12 500
B: 5 × 2.5 = 12.5
C: 0.5 × 2.5 = 1.25
D: 50 × 25 = 1250
E: 5 × 25 = 125
From smallest to largest it would be C, B, E, D and A. So E would be in the middle.

23. 2000 kg

80 is double 40 and 25 kg is double 12.5 kg so you need to multiply 500 kg by 4. 4 × 500 kg = 2000 kg.

Page 14

You can do these divisions by partitioning the bigger number and dividing each of the parts by the other number. Alternatively, you could use short division. Which method you choose depends on the numbers you're working with.

1. 16

Break 96 into numbers that easily divide by 6. 96 breaks into 60 + 36. Divide these bits separately then add them together at the end. 60 ÷ 6 = 10, 36 ÷ 6 = 6, 10 + 6 = 16.

2. 31

124 breaks into 100 + 24. 100 ÷ 4 = 25, 24 ÷ 4 = 6, 25 + 6 = 31

3. 144

720 breaks into 500 + 200 + 20. 500 ÷ 5 = 100, 200 ÷ 5 = 40, 20 ÷ 5 = 4, 100 + 40 + 4 = 144.

4. 107

```
    1 0 7
8 | 8 5 ⁵6
```

5. 22.4

```
    2 2 . 4
3 | 6 7 .¹2
```

6. remainder 2

```
    0 7 remainder 2
5 | 3 ³7
```

7. remainder 3

```
    0 2 5 remainder 3
4 | 1 ¹0 ²3
```

8. remainder 6

```
    0 1 5 remainder 6
8 | 1 ¹2 ⁴6
```

9. remainder 6

```
    0 2 0 remainder 6
9 | 1 ¹8 6
```

10. remainder 4

```
    0 3 0 remainder 4
8 | 2 ²4 4
```

11. 13

There are 81 + 10 = 91 students and staff altogether.

```
    1 3
7 | 9 ²1
```

12. 70 cm

$$8 \overline{)5^5 6\ 0} = 0\ 7\ 0$$

13. 18

$$8 \overline{)1^1 3^5 9} = 0\ 1\ 7 \text{ remainder } 3$$

3 are remaining, so Claire will need 1 more box, 18.

14. 33

$$9 \overline{)3^3 0^3 0} = 0\ 3\ 3 \text{ remainder } 3$$

Mr Bond can set out 33 complete rows.

15. B

Find the number that 128 divides by exactly.

$$3 \overline{)1^1 2\ 8} = 0\ 4\ 2 \text{ remainder } 2$$

$$4 \overline{)1^1 2\ 8} = 0\ 3\ 2$$

It's divisible by 4 with no remainders.

Pages 15-16

Replace a with 6 in each calculation.

1. 11
$6 + 5 = 11$

2. 24
$4 \times 6 = 24$

3. 9
$(2 \times 6) - 3 = 12 - 3 = 9$

4. 30
$(3 \times 6) + (2 \times 6) = 18 + 12 = 30$

5. 50
$5(6 + 4) = 5 \times 10 = 50$

6. 2a
2 lots of a = 2 × a, or 2a.

7. 3n – 2
3 × n = 3n, 3n – 2.

8. 4x + 3x
5x + 2x = 7x, and 3x + 4x = 7x

9. 6a + 3b
3(2a + b) means: (2a + b) + (2a + b) + (2a + b) = 6a + 3b.

10. 2m – 2(m + 0)
2(m + 0) means (m + 0) + (m + 0), which is 2m.
So the expression is 2m – 2m.

11. C
4 × 7 = 28. Whatever x represents, the product of 3 × x must be smaller than 28. The biggest number x could be is 9. 3 × 9 = 27.

12. D
If e = 8, then time = 60 + (5 × 8) = 60 + 40 = 100 minutes.

13. C
3 pieces x cm long are 3x cm long in total. The plank was 400 cm long, so after the three pieces are cut off it is (400 – 3x) cm long.

14. £525
d = 9, so cost = 75 + (50 × 9) = 75 + 450 = £525.

15. E
Each passenger, or p, costs £5. So that can be shown as 5 × p, or 5p. The total cost is 5p plus £260 = 260 + 5p.

16. A
Each game, or n, costs £35. So that can be shown as 35 × n, or 35n. The total cost is 35n plus the cost of the console = 150 + 35n.

17. 4n – 1
Choose a term and test each expression to find out which gives the correct value. E.g. for the second term, n = 2: substitute 2 for n in each expression and see which gives the correct value, 7.
Only 4n – 1 gives 7 when n = 2: (4 × 2) – 1 = 7
If there had been more than one expression which gave the correct value, you would have had to choose a different term and test which one of the expressions was correct.

18. £69
Put m = 25 into the formula.
15 + 2(25 + 2) = 15 + 2 × 27 = 15 + 54 = £69

19. 36
The expression for the sequence is ½ n(n + 1), so substitute 8 into the expression and follow the rules of BODMAS.
½ × 8(8 + 1) = ½ × 8 × 9 = ½ × 72 = 36

20. 5F + ½ × 8F
If a full page advert costs F, then 5 full page adverts will cost 5 × F or 5F. If a half page advert costs ½F, then 8 half page adverts will cost 8 × ½F. So the formula would be 5F + ½ × 8F.

Section Three
— Number Problems

Page 17

Use BODMAS to do each part of these equations in the correct order.

1. 28
$7 + 4 \times 6 - 3 = 7 + 24 - 3 = 31 - 3 = 28$

2. 9
$6 + 8 \div 2 - 1 = 6 + 4 - 1 = 10 - 1 = 9$

3. 3
$7 + 6 - 5 \times 2 = 7 + 6 - 10 = 13 - 10 = 3$

4. 63
$9 \times 5 + 6 \times 3 = 45 + 18 = 63$

5. 18
$3 \times 5 + 15 \div 5 = 15 + 3 = 18$

For questions 6-10, work out the part of the calculation you're given if you can, then try the different signs until you find the one that works. Remember to use BODMAS to find the correct answer.

6. ×
6 + 4 is in brackets, so you know it must be done first:
7 _ (6 + 4) = 7 _ 10 = 70. 7 × 10 = 70

7. –
3 × 2 is in brackets, so you know it must be done first:
9 _ (3 × 2) = 9 _ 6 = 3, 9 – 6 = 3

8.   +

8×1 is in brackets, so you know it must be done first:
$3 \_ (8 \times 1) = 3 \_ 8 = 11$, $3 + 8 = 11$

9.   ÷

$11 - 2$ is in brackets, so you know it must be done first:
$27 \_ (11 - 2) = 27 \_ 9 = 3$. $27 \div 9 = 3$.

10.   ×

$4 \_ 5$ is in brackets, so you know it must be done first. This bit's a bit trickier because you need to do the unknown calculation first. One more than (4_5) is 21 from the equation. So (4_5) must be 1 less than $21 = 20$. $4 \times 5 = 20$.

11.   29 600

Estimate to find the answer, 89×296 can be rounded to $90 \times 300 = 27\,000$. 11×296 can be rounded to $10 \times 300 = 3000$. $27\,000 + 3000 = 30\,000$. The only answer that's close to this is $29\,600$. Alternatively, you could add 89 and 11 together to get 100, then multiply this by 296. $100 \times 296 = 29\,600$

12.   D

Find the options with the biggest multiplication and work them out. 7×6 is the biggest multiplication, so
B: $7 \times 6 = 42$, $42 - 4 = 38$, $38 + 3 = 41$
D: $7 \times 6 = 42$, $4 - 3 = 1$, $42 + 1 = 43$
So D is the answer.

13.   – 40p

The price of each ticket has been rounded up by 5p. There are 8 tickets in total, $8 \times 5 = 40$. So to complete the equation you need to subtract 40p.

14.   E

A: $10 \div 5 = 2$, $60 - 20 = 40$, $40 + 2 = 42$
B: $20 \div 10 = 2$, $60 - 2 = 58$, $58 + 5 = 63$
C: $10 \div 5 = 2$, $60 + 20 = 80$, $80 - 2 = 78$
D: $20 \div 10 = 2$, $60 + 2 = 62$, $62 - 5 = 57$
E: $60 \div 20 = 3$, $3 + 10 = 13$, $13 - 5 = 8$
E is the answer.

15.   2

To work out 60×3.5 you can partition 3.5 into $3 + 0.5$. $60 \times 3 = 180$, $60 \times 0.5 = 30$, $180 + 30 = 210$. This leaves you with $420 \div 210$. Dividing both numbers by 10 gives you $42 \div 21$. $42 \div 21 = 2$

Pages 18-19

1.   £80

Matt worked for 3 hours + 4 hours + 3 hours, so that's 10 hours in total. $10 \times £8 = £80$

2.   £2

If one shirt costs £11, then two shirts would be $2 \times £11 = £22$. $£24 - £22 = £2$, which is the cost of the tie.

3.   4

Half of 56 is 28 ($56 \div 2 = 28$). Finlay eats 8 chocolates per day.
Day 1: $56 - 8 = 48$ left.
Day 2: $48 - 8 = 40$ left.
Day 3: $40 - 8 = 32$ left,
Day 4: $32 - 8 = 24$ left, which is less than half.

4.   81

The only number which is a multiple of 9 is 81. 81 sweets can be shared equally between 9 friends, giving each of them 9 sweets.

5.   78

3 litres of paint will paint $\frac{3}{5}$ of the parking spaces that 5 litres will paint. $130 \div 5 = 26$, $26 \times 3 = 78$

6.   C

Find the total price for each answer option until you find the correct answer.
C: 1 calculator + 1 ruler + 1 rubber = $£4.50 + £1.00 + 75p = £6.25$. C is the answer.

7.   450 g

Find the weight of one ball. $750\,g \div 5 = 150\,g$. Two balls are used, so that's $150\,g \times 2 = 300\,g$, which would leave $750\,g - 300\,g = 450\,g$.

8.   0.8 kg

6 people need 1.2 kg, so 1 person needs $1.2\,kg \div 6 = 0.2\,kg$. 4 people would need $4 \times 0.2 = 0.8\,kg$.

9.   8

Work back from 6.4, so $6.4 \times 10 = 64$. The number which was squared to give 64 is 8 ($8 \times 8 = 64$).

10.   £36.25

2 shirts = $2 \times £12.50 = £25$
Boots = £32
3 pairs of socks = $3 \times £2.25 = £6.75$
$25 + 32 + 6.75 = £63.75$.
$100 - 63.75 = £36.25$

11.   £8.25

The pack of two large candles costs $3 \times £5.50 = £16.50$. Each large candle costs $£16.50 \div 2 = £8.25$

12.   £1.15

If Connor received 10p change from £7, he spent £6.90. $£7 - £6.90 = 10p$. 1 choc ice = $£6.90 \div 6 = £1.15$

13.   16.5 g

He spent 24p. If 1 snake costs 4p, then 24p buys $24 \div 4 = 6$ snakes. $2\frac{3}{4}\,g$ is the same as 2.75 g, so 6 snakes would weigh $6 \times 2.75\,g = 16.5\,g$

14.   E

A: This can be true, e.g. Chris could have sold 28 teas and 27 coffees.
B: This can be true, e.g. people could have bought 28 coffees and 27 teas.
C: This can be true, e.g. Chris could have sold 31 teas and 26 coffees.
D: This can be true, e.g. Chris could have sold 38 coffees and 19 teas.
E: This cannot be true. The total number of teas and coffees sold is odd (57), so the sum of the number of teas and coffees sold must be an odd number added to an even number. The difference between an odd number and an even number is always odd. 10 is an even number, so this cannot be true.

15.   170 cm

There are 10 rows of bricks. There will be 10 concrete layers altogether — 9 between the rows plus one beneath the bottom row.
Total height of bricks = $15 \times 10 = 150\,cm$.
Total height of concrete layers = $2 \times 10 = 20\,cm$.
So the total height of the wall = $150 + 20 = 170\,cm$.

16. 4 litres

A 2 litre bottle can make 6 × 800 ml of squash.
6 × 800 ml = 4800 ml. The total volume of squash needed is
48 × 200 ml. 48 × 200 ml = 9600 ml. 9600 ml is double
4800 ml, so the amount of concentrate needed is
2 × 2 litres = 4 litres.

17. £96

The children spent 24p on soap and wax for each car, so in total
they spent 24p × 100 = £24. The total amount charged is
£1.20 × 100 = £120. The amount they raised for charity is the
total amount charged, minus the total amount spent on soap and
wax. £120 – £24 = £96
Alternatively, you could work out the profit on each car wash,
which would be the amount charged, minus the cost of the soap
and wax, £1.20 – 24p = 96p. Now multiply this by the number of
cars washed, 96p × 100 = £96.

18. £1.98

The ingredients shown are enough for 24 rock cakes and Ben wants
to make 36. 36 ÷ 24 = 1.5, so you need to multiply the amount
of each ingredient in the recipe by 1.5. There are 2 eggs in the
recipe, so 2 × 1.5 = 3 eggs. 3 × 22p = 66p. The ingredients
shown are enough for 20 lemon buns, and Ben wants to make 60.
60 ÷ 20 = 3, so you need to multiply the amount of each ingredient
in the recipe by 3. There are 2 eggs in the recipe, so 2 × 3 = 6 eggs.
6 × 22p = £1.32. £1.32 + 66p = £1.98

19. 12

Round £9.50 to £10. 120 ÷ 10 = 12. So £120 is enough for
12 children. £9.50 was rounded up, so to find how much was left
over, £10 – £9.50 = 50p, 12 × 50p = £6, £6 is not enough for
another child.

20. 250 cm

Each box weighs 450 g and there are 9 kg of boxes.
9 kg = 9000 g (because 1 kg = 1000 g). 9000 ÷ 450 = 20.
So there are 20 boxes. 1 box is 12.5 cm, so 20 would be
12.5 cm × 20 = 250 cm.

Section Four
— Data Handling

Page 20

For questions 1 and 2 you need to read the values from the table.

1. 15
2. 12
3. 8

17 pupils in class C use a PC and 9
use a laptop. 17 – 9 = 8 pupils.

4. Class C

17 pupils in class C use a PC, compared to 12 in class B and 8
in class A.

5. 17

6 pupils in class A, 5 pupils in class B and 6 pupils in class C do
not use a computer. Add up the values from each class to find the
total number.   6 + 5 + 6 = 17

6. 8

The values in the table must add up to 40 (the number of children
asked). Therefore add up the numbers given and subtract this
from 40 to find the missing number.   8 + 4 + 8 + 5 + 7 = 32
40 – 32 = 8

7. 27

Add together the number of children who receive less than £1 and
the number who receive between £1 and £3.50. 15 + 12 = 27

8. 9

You can't find the number of large cheese and ham pizzas sold
straight away. There are two methods that you can use:

Method 1: First find the total of cheese and ham pizzas sold by
subtracting the total number of pepperoni sold from the overall
total sold: 24 – 8 = 16. There were 16 cheese and ham sold in
total and 7 were small so the number of large cheese and ham is
16 – 7 = 9.

Method 2: First find the total number of large pizzas sold by
subtracting the total number of small pizzas sold from the overall
total sold: 24 – 9 = 15. There were 15 large pizzas sold and 6 of
these were pepperoni so the number of large cheese and ham is
15 – 6 = 9.

Pages 21-22

1. Newspapers

There was only 1 newspaper found.
This is less than any other type of litter.

2. 5

Read the value from the graph.

3. 4

There were 7 sweet wrappers found and 3 bottles found.
7 – 3 = 4

4. 4

There was 1 newspaper found and 5 crisp packets found.
5 – 1 = 4

5. Cans

There were 3 bottles found. 3 × 2 = 6 so the answer is the item
that was found 6 times. There were 6 cans found.

6. 45

Each symbol on the pictogram represents 20 fish. There are 2 $\frac{1}{4}$
symbols for Blue Acara. $\frac{1}{4}$ of 20 = 5, 2 × 20 = 40 so the number
of Blue Acara = 5 + 40 = 45.

7. 75

The bar chart shows that 375 people watched the 7 pm film on
Friday. There are 450 seats available so the number of empty
seats is 450 – 375 = 75.

8. 13

Each symbol = 4 drinks. There are 4 $\frac{3}{4}$ symbols for blackcurrant
drinks. 4 × 4 = 16 drinks. $\frac{3}{4}$ of 4 = 3 drinks. So the total
number of blackcurrant drinks = 16 + 3 = 19. Cherryade is
represented by 1 $\frac{1}{2}$ symbols. 4 × 1 = 4, $\frac{1}{2}$ of 4 = 2. So the
total number of cherryade drinks = 4 + 2 = 6. So the difference
between the number of blackcurrant and cherryade drinks =
19 – 6 = 13 drinks. Alternatively, you could find the difference
in the number of symbols for blackcurrant and cherryade drinks,
then multiply this by 4: 4 $\frac{3}{4}$ – 1 $\frac{1}{2}$ = 3 $\frac{1}{4}$ symbols. 4 × 3 = 12,
$\frac{1}{4}$ of 4 = 1. So the difference in the number of drinks is
12 + 1 = 13 drinks.

9. £30

The graph tells you that $4.50 equals £3. $45 is ten times
greater than $4.50, so multiply £3 by ten to find the number of
pounds. £3 × 10 = £30

10.   72

18 teenagers preferred to spend their money on technology and this represents one quarter of the pie chart. Multiply 18 by 4 to find the total number of teenagers in the survey. 18 × 4 = 72.

11.   3 minutes

The flat portion of the graph between 11 and 14 minutes shows that Joe is not moving. This must be when he stopped to talk to his friend. 14 − 11 = 3 minutes

12.   750

The shot put section has an angle of 60° and represents 250 tickets. The high jump section covers half of the pie chart. As the total of the angles in a pie chart is 360°, the size of the high jump angle is 180° (360 ÷ 2). The size of the high jump section is three times the size of the shot put section (60 × 3 = 180) so the high jump sold three times as many tickets. 3 × 250 = 750 tickets.

Page 23

The mode is the most common number in a group. For questions 1-5, you need to find the number that occurs most often in each set.

1.   6
2.   19
3.   18
4.   3
5.   19

The median is the middle value in a group. To answer questions 6-10, you need to arrange the values from smallest to biggest, and find the middle value in each row. If there is an even number of values, then find the number halfway between the two middle values.

6.   12
7.   18
8.   8
9.   58
10.   27.5

11.   2

To calculate the mean, add up all the numbers of goals: (0 + 2 + 4 + 2 + 5 + 1 + 0 + 2 = 16) and then divide by the number of matches they played (8). 16 ÷ 8 = 2

12.   10

The range is the difference between the highest and lowest value on the graph. 20 chickens hatched on Thursday and 10 chickens hatched on Wednesday. 20 − 10 = 10

13.   Tuesday

The range is the difference between the highest and lowest temperature. The range on Tuesday is 14 − 6 = 8 °C. This is higher than any other day.

14.   10

Mean = total score of the six tests ÷ number of tests (6). So, to work out the total score of the six tests, multiply the mean by 6: 7 × 6 = 42. To find the missing score, subtract the other scores from 42. 42 − 4 − 6 − 7 − 10 − 5 = 10

Page 24

1.   Anne

Despite only having 12 votes, Anne received a higher percentage than Jamie, Hasim, Ted and Lex. Jamie got 25%, Hasim got 10% and Ted got 5%. Lex didn't get any votes, so he got 0%. So that leaves Anne with 100% − 40% (25 + 10 + 5) = 60% (There were only twenty voters).

2.   C

The pictures in this pictogram are different sizes and this is misleading. For example the crocodile row appears longer than the snake row, but there are only 12 crocodiles (3 × 4 = 12) compared to 22 snakes (5.5 × 4 = 22).

3.   D

The steps on the vertical axis double each time. What the graph appears to show at a glance is different to what the data actually shows. For example, the number of calls on Wednesday is actually double the number on Tuesday, but the difference between the values plotted on the graph looks smaller than this.

4.   D

The number of children with blue eyes is $\frac{3}{4}$ of the number with green eyes. There are 24 children with blue eyes and 32 with green eyes. $\frac{1}{4}$ of 32 is 8 (32 ÷ 4 = 8) so $\frac{3}{4}$ of 32 = 3 × 8 = 24. (The blue bar is not $\frac{3}{4}$ of the height of the green bar because the scale does not start at zero.)

Page 25

1. $\frac{3}{8}$

Three of the eight sections contain the number 4 so the probability is $\frac{3}{8}$.

2. $\frac{5}{8}$

Five of the sections contain an odd number so the probability is $\frac{5}{8}$.

3.   0

The number 7 isn't on the spinner. (Also accept zero, none or impossible.)

4.   5

The number 5 only occurs in one section. This is less than all of the other numbers so spinning a 5 is least likely.

5.   3

Four of the eight sections contain a 3, so the probability of spinning a 3 is $\frac{4}{8}$ or $\frac{1}{2}$.

6. $\frac{3}{6}$ or $\frac{1}{2}$

Three out of the six numbers on a dice are even, so the probability of rolling an even number is $\frac{3}{6}$ or $\frac{1}{2}$.

7. $\frac{5}{12}$

Five of the 12 marbles are red so the probability of picking a red marble is $\frac{5}{12}$.

8. $\frac{7}{12}$

Seven of the 12 marbles are green so the probability of picking a green marble is $\frac{7}{12}$.

9. $\frac{3}{9}$ or $\frac{1}{3}$

Three of the nine socks are striped, so the probability of picking a striped sock is $\frac{3}{9}$ or $\frac{1}{3}$.

10. ⁶⁄₁₁

There are 11 letters in the word so 11 possible outcomes.
There are 2Ms, 2As and 1S (5 tiles) so only the remaining
6 tiles (11 – 5 = 6) will give a letter that is not M, S, or A.
So the probability is ⁶⁄₁₁.

11. 7

One quarter of the scarves are yellow so the number of yellow
scarves = 16 ÷ 4 = 4. You know that 5 scarves are green so the
rest are red. 16 – 4 – 5 = 7

12. B

There are 16 jars of jam (6 + 3 + 4 + 3 = 16) and 4 of them are
strawberry. So the probability of picking strawberry is ⁴⁄₁₆ or ¼.

13. ⁴⁄₂₂ or ²⁄₁₁

At the start ¼ of the sweets in the bag are bears (24 ÷ 4 = 6).
After 2 bears are removed this leaves a total of 22 sweets of
which 4 are bears. This means the probability of choosing a bear
next is ⁴⁄₂₂ or ²⁄₁₁.

Section Five
— Shape and Space

Page 26

1. 40°
The three angles in a triangle add up to 180°.
Angle x = 180 – 65 – 75 = 40°.

2. Acute
Angles that are smaller than a right angle (90°) are acute angles.

3. 105°
Angles on a straight line add up to 180°.
Angle y = 180 – 75 = 105°.

4. Obtuse
Angles that are bigger than 90° but smaller than 180° are
obtuse angles.

5. 295°
Angles around a point add up to 360°. Angle z = 360 – 65 = 295°.

6. 180°
Angles on a straight line add up to 180°.

7. 123°
Angles on a straight line add up to 180°.
Angle U = 180 – 34 – 23 = 123°.

8. 23°
The three angles in a triangle add up to 180°.
180 – 90 – 67 = 23°.

9. 45°
The angle looks to be half of the size of a right angle. A right angle
is 90°, so the size of the angle is about 90 ÷ 2 = 45°.

10. A
An obtuse angle is an angle that is bigger than 90° and smaller
than 180°. Shape A contains two obtuse angles.

11. 210°
Each angle in an equilateral triangle is 60° and each angle in a
square is a right angle (90°). The shaded angle is made up of
one angle from the square and two angles from the equilateral
triangles: 90 + 60 + 60 = 210°.

12. 70°
The angles in a quadrilateral add up to 360°. The size of the
fourth angle inside the shape = 360 – 85 – 83 – 82 = 110°.
The angles on a straight line add up to 180°
so angle y = 180 – 110 = 70°.

13. 10
There are 360° in a full circle and the numbers on a clock face
divide the circle into 12 equal sectors. Each sector has an angle
of 360 ÷ 12 = 30°. The minute hand has moved 300° so it has
moved through 10 sectors (30 × 10 = 300). If the minute hand
moves on 10 sectors from 12 it is pointing at 10.

Pages 27-28

1. C
Shape C has two right angles.

2. D
An isosceles triangle has three sides in total, with two that are
equal in length — D is the only shape with three sides and two
that are equal in length.

3. C
A pentagon has five sides — C is the only shape with five sides.

4. H
A quadrilateral has four sides. H is a quadrilateral with four sides
that are equal in length.

5. B
The two horizontal lines in B are parallel and
the shape has no right angles.

6. BC (or CB)
Parallel lines have the same slope so BC is parallel to DE.

7. AB (or BA)
ABE is an isosceles triangle so AB is equal in length to AE.

8. Kite
The points form a quadrilateral with two pairs of non-parallel sides
of equal length (AE = AB and EF = FB), and a pair of opposite
obtuse angles that are equal (at points B and E).

9. Pentagon
Joining points BCDEF makes a shape with five sides.
A pentagon is the name given to a shape with five sides.

10. CE (or EC)
Perpendicular lines are at 90° to each other. The diagonal line CE
is perpendicular and the same length as DB.

11. D
Shape D is a hexagon so it cannot be placed in either the triangle
or quadrilateral rows of the table.

12. Square
A square has four straight sides that are all the
same length and four right angles.

13. Trapezium

A trapezium has one pair of parallel sides. These are shown on the diagram:

14. Right-angled triangle

Perpendicular sides are at right angles to each other (see the diagram).

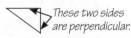 These two sides are perpendicular.

15. Rhombus

The diagram shows the reflected shape.
It is a rhombus because it has 4 equal sides, 2 equal obtuse angles and 2 equal acute angles.

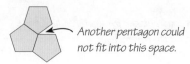

16. Parallelogram

The properties of a parallelogram match those given. It cannot be a rectangle as it has acute and obtuse angles and it would need all 4 sides to be of equal length for it to be a rhombus. As it has two pairs of parallel lines it can't be a kite, a trapezium or any other irregular quadrilateral.

17. 450 mm

The radius of a circle is half of the diameter: $900 \div 2 = 450$ mm.

18. C

Pentagons do not fit together without gaps whereas the other 4 shapes do. For example:

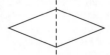 Another pentagon could not fit into this space.

19. Octagon

The internal angle of a regular polygon increases as the number of sides increases. An octagon has 8 sides which is more than the other shapes given.

20. 150°

The angles of any quadrilateral add up to 360°. The marked angles inside the rhombus are both 30° so the total of the unknown angles must be 300° (360 – 30 – 30). Opposite angles in a rhombus are equal so angle a must be 300 ÷ 2 = 150°.

21. A

A rectangle does have four right angles, but it also has pairs of equal sides. So it should also be in the 'at least one pair of equal sides' circle. (It should be in the same region as the square.)

22. Kite

A square, rectangle, parallelogram, rhombus and trapezium all have parallel sides.

Pages 29-30

To find the area of the shapes in questions 1 - 3, count the number of squares inside each shape. Each side of a square on the grid is 1 cm, so the area of each square is 1 cm².

1. 16 cm²
2. 26 cm²
3. 6 cm²

To find the perimeter of the shapes for questions 4-5, work out the length of each side by counting the squares. Add up the length of every side to find the perimeter of each shape.

4. 24 cm
5. 22 cm

For questions 6-8, work out the perimeter of each shape by adding the lengths of each side together. In question 6, shape S is a rectangle, so the missing sides are 7 cm and 3 cm.

6. 20 cm
7. 27 cm
8. 22 cm
9. 21 cm²

Find the area of a rectangle by multiplying the length and width together: $7 \times 3 = 21$ cm²

10. 24 cm²

The area of a triangle is $\frac{1}{2} \times$ base $\times$ height.
$\frac{1}{2} \times 4 \times 12 = 2 \times 12 = 24$ cm²

11. 125 cm

A regular pentagon has 5 equal sides so all 5 sides are 25 cm long. $25 + 25 + 25 + 25 + 25$ (or 5×25) $= 125$ cm.

12. 5 m

The area of the carpet = length x width. $75 = 15 \times$ width, so width $= 75 \div 15 = 5$ m

13. 70 m

The playground is a regular octagon so all eight sides are the same length. The perimeter (560 m) divided by the number of sides (8) gives the length of each side: $560 \div 8 = 70$ m.

14. 16

From the left hand vertical side lengths you know the total height of the pen is 2 m + 4 m = 6 m. So the missing height on the right hand side of the pen must be 6 m – 4 m = 2 m. From the horizontal length at the top you know the total length of the pen is 10 m. So the missing length on the left hand side is 10 m – 4 m – 4 m = 2 m. The sides of the pen are 10 m, 4 m, 4 m, 2 m, 4 m, 4 m, 2 m and 2 m — giving a total of 32 m. Each panel is 2 m long so the number of panels needed is 32 ÷ 2 = 16 panels.

15. C and D

Count the number of squares in each shape to find its area. The area of shape C = 10 squares + 4 half squares = 12 squares. The area of shape D is also 12 squares.

16. 540 cm

The outer edge of the patio consists of 18 of the 30 cm sides. So the perimeter is 18 x 30 = 540 cm.

17. 270 cm²

The three cardboard panels that make the tunnel each have the same dimensions and therefore the same area. Area of each panel = 15 x 6 = 90 cm². Total area = 3 x 90 = 270 cm².

18. 57 cm²

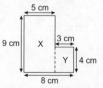

Split the shape into two rectangles — e.g. X and Y. X has sides 9 cm and 5 cm long so the area is 9 x 5 = 45 cm². Y has sides 3 cm (8 – 5) and 4 cm long so the area is 3 x 4 = 12 cm². The total area of the shape is 45 + 12 = 57 cm².

19. 130 cm

The hole is made up of twenty two 5 cm edges and two
10 cm edges. The perimeter is:
$(22 \times 5) + (2 \times 10) = 110 + 20 = 130$ cm.

20. 700 m²

The total area of the supermarket and the car park is 40×25
$= 1000$ m². The area of the supermarket is $20 \times 15 = 300$ m².
Subtract the area of the supermarket from the total area to find
the area of the car park: $1000 - 300 = 700$ m².

21. 22 cm

A rectangle with an area of 24 cm² must have sides of 2 cm and
12 cm, 3 cm and 8 cm, 4 cm and 6 cm or 1 cm and 24 cm. As
the difference in the length of the sides is given as 5 cm then the
rectangle must have sides of 3 cm and 8 cm. So its perimeter
must be $3 + 3 + 8 + 8$ (or $(3 + 8) \times 2) = 22$ cm.

22. 3

The area of each wall is $4 \times 2 = 8$ m². The total area of all
4 walls is $4 \times 8 = 32$ m². Two tins of paint will be enough for
24 m² of wall $(2 \times 12 = 24)$ and three tins will be enough for
36 m² of wall $(3 \times 12 = 36)$. So Martha needs to buy 3 tins
of paint to have enough.

Page 31

1. 3

R, F and N have no lines of symmetry.

2. H

H has one vertical and one horizontal line of symmetry.

3. W

W only has a vertical line of symmetry.

4. D

D only has a horizontal line of symmetry.

5. D

Shape D has a horizontal mirror line.

6. B

B has rotational symmetry.
It fits into itself twice when you rotate it 360°.

7. Hexagon

The reflected shape has six sides (see diagram).
This means that it is a hexagon.

8. 5

9. B

Shape B is the only shape that has a diagonal mirror line.

1. 5

Shape A is a pentagonal prism. It has 5 rectangular faces.

2. E

A cube has six identical square faces.

3. D

A triangular prism has 2 triangular faces at each end and
3 rectangular faces in the middle. It also has 9 edges.

4. C

A cone has two faces but only one curved edge between the flat
face and the curved face.

5. B

A square-based pyramid has five faces (1 square base + 4
triangular faces), 8 edges and 5 vertices (the vertices of the
square plus the vertex at the tip of the pyramid).

6. 14 cm³

There are 14 cubes and the volume of each cube is 1 cm³, so the
volume = 14×1 cm³ = 14 cm³.

7. 84

7 cubes fit along the length of the box, 3 cubes fit across the
width and 4 cubes can stack up the height of the box.
$7 \times 3 \times 4 = 84$ cubes.

8. A

Net A is the only net that will fold up to make a cube.

9. B

A cuboid has more than 2 quadrilateral faces and it is also a
prism. So it should go in the overlap of these two circles.
It has no curved edges so it cannot go in the third circle.

10. D

The net folds up to make a square-based pyramid. Points Z and D
will join together at the top of the pyramid.

11. D

The same letter cannot be on squares that are next to each other
if they are to be opposite each other when the net is folded.

12. 180

The edges of each cube are 4 cm long. The box is wide enough to
fit $40 \div 4 = 10$ cubes. The width of the box means you could fit
$24 \div 4 = 6$ rows in it. So one layer of cubes = $6 \times 10 = 60$ cubes.
The box is high enough to fit $12 \div 4 = 3$ layers of cubes in it. So
the total number of cubes = $3 \times 60 = 180$.

13. B

There is no net for the cone. The diagram shows what the net of a
cone might look like:

14. 8 cm

Volume = length × width × height. $800 = 20 \times$ width $\times 5$,
so $800 = 100 \times$ width. So, width = $800 \div 100 = 8$ cm.

15. 44 m³

Volume = length × width × height so the volume of the larger
cuboid is $4 \times 3 \times 3 = 36$ m³. The volume of the small cube is
$2 \times 2 \times 2 = 8$ m³. The total volume is $36 + 8 = 44$ m³

Page 34

For questions 1-5, you need to imagine the shape being flipped and moved to find the answer option that matches the transformed shape.

1. **C**
2. **A**
3. **D**
4. **B**
5. **E**

6. **2 cm**

7 sides of each of the outer 4 octagons make up the perimeter of the shape, plus 4 sides of the central octagon. So the total number of octagon sides that make up the shape = (7 × 4) + 4 = 28 + 4 = 32. The total perimeter of the shape = 64 cm. So the length of each octagon side = 64 ÷ 32 = 2 cm.

7. **18**

The diagram below shows the painted faces on the stairs:
11 painted faces are visible.

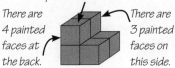

There are 4 painted faces at the back.

There are 3 painted faces on this side.

11 + 4 + 3 = 18 painted faces.

8. **1 and 6**

Shape 1 reflected and rotated gives shape 6.

9. **E**

When shape Z is rotated through 90° clockwise you get shape E.

Pages 35-36

To find the coordinates for questions 1-5, move along the x-axis to find the horizontal position of the point. Then move up the y-axis to find the vertical position.

1. **(9, 7)**
2. **(5, 11)**
3. **(4, 4)**
4. **(8, 2)**
5. **(2, 9)**

6. **(4, 9)**

When you move 4 squares west from point A you get to the point (4, 2). When you move 7 squares north from (4, 2) you reach the point (4, 9).

7. **(–7, 0)**

To be parallel with JK, the line must follow the dotted line on the diagram. Plot the coordinates you're given until you find the pair that sit on this line. The only option given that's on this line is point (-7, 0).

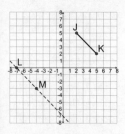

8. **(8, 6)**

The rotated triangle is shown in the diagram. The coordinates of point B are now at (8, 6).

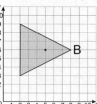

9. **(10, 7)**

To find the length of the shortest side, find the difference between the two y-axis values (7 – 3 = 4). The length of the longest side is double this: 4 × 2 = 8. The x-axis coordinate is 8 along from 2, 2 + 8 = 10. The y-axis coordinate is the same as the corner at (2, 7). The coordinates of point W are (10, 7).

10. **(6, 15)**

W is vertically below point (6, 19) (top of the pentagon). So its x-coordinate is also 6. W is also in a horizontal line with points (3, 15) and (9, 15), so its y-coordinate is also 15.

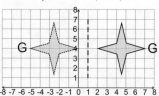

11. **(-5, 4)**

The diagram shows the reflected shape. The coordinates of the reflected point G are (-5, 4).

12. **(8, 4)**

Only points with x and y coordinates greater than 2 but less than 7 will lie within the square. (8, 4) has an x-coordinate greater than 7 so is outside of the square.

13. **(12, 8)**

The point at (1, 8) has moved to (4, 10). The x-coordinate has increased by 3 and the y-coordinate has increased by 2 (so the shape has moved 3 squares right and 2 squares up). Point C was previously at (9, 6) so its new x-coordinate is 9 + 3 = 12, and its new y-coordinate is 6 + 2 = 8.

14. **(3, 4)**

The points A and B have a horizontal difference of 4 (5 – 1) and a vertical difference of 4 (6 – 2). So the horizontal distance between C and A is 4 ÷ 2 = 2. The vertical distance of C from A is 4 ÷ 2 = 2. This means the x-coordinate of C is 2 more than A: 1 + 2 = 3. The y-coordinate of C is also 2 more than A: 2 + 2 = 4.

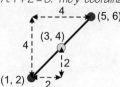

Section Six
— Units and Measures

Pages 37-38

Pick the unit that best matches each object.

1. cm
A pencil is usually no longer than 20 cm, so you'd measure it in centimetres.

2. km
It's a long way between London and Liverpool, so you'd measure the distance in kilometres.

3. m
Doors are a bit taller than the average person, so you'd measure their height in metres.

4. mm
The thickness of a coin is very small, so you'd measure it in millimetres.

5. 1560 g
1 kilogram = 1000 grams. 1.56 × 1000 = 1560 grams

6. 2500 ml
1 litre = 1000 millilitres. 2.5 × 1000 = 2500 millilitres

7. 1.28 m
1 metre = 100 centimetres. 128 ÷ 100 = 1.28 metres

8. 15 300 m
1 kilometre = 1000 metres. 15.3 × 1000 = 15 300 metres

9. 4.5 kg
1 kilogram = 1000 grams. 4500 ÷ 1000 = 4.5 kilograms

10. 5.4 g
2.54 kg, 5400 g, 5.4 kg and 54 kg are far too heavy for a pencil. The most likely answer is 5.4 g.

11. 175 g
The scale increases by 25 g at every point. The needle on the scale is pointing at one point before 200 g, so 200 g – 25 g = 175 g.

12. Saucepan
An egg cup, a teacup and teaspoon are all very small and wouldn't hold 1 litre of water. A dustbin is very large and would hold several litres of water. The most likely answer is a saucepan.

13. 100
1 km = 1000 m, so to convert 1.4 km into metres: 1.4 × 1000 = 1400 m. To find out how many rolls you need, divide 1400 by 14. 1400 ÷ 14 = 100.

14. 500 g
Find the mass of 1 bag, 16 kg ÷ 32 = 0.5 kg. You need to give your answer in grams. 1 kg = 1000 g, so 0.5 × 1000 = 500 g.

15. 26.4 m
Convert all lengths to metres. 1 metre = 100 cm, so 650 cm is 650 ÷ 100 = 6.5 m. Add all the lengths together, 6.5 + 7.6 + 12.3 = 26.4 m.

16. 18 m
Find 6 × 300. 6 × 3 = 18, so 6 × 300 = 1800 cm. 1 m = 100 cm, so 1800 ÷ 100 = 18 m.

17. E
1 litre = 1000 ml, so 1.5 litres is 1500 ml. 400 ml is about a quarter of 1500 ml, so the correct bottle will be about three quarters full.

18. 6 litres
Convert 750 ml into litres. 1 litre = 1000 ml, so 750 ÷ 1000 = 0.75. 2 bottles would contain 2 × 0.75 = 1.5 litres. So 8 bottles would contain 4 × 1.5 = 6 litres.

19. C
To find the amount of cereal produced in an hour you need to solve 42 × 250 g. 1 kg = 1000 g, so 250 g is the same as 250 ÷ 1000 = 0.25 kg. The total mass of cereal is 42 × 0.25 kg. 4 lots of 0.25 kg is equal to 1 kg. So the total mass of cereal is 42 ÷ 4 = 10.5 kg

20. 200 ml
12 × 150 ml = 1800 ml. 2 litres = 1000 ml × 2 = 2000 ml, so 2000 ml – 1800 ml = 200 ml.

21. 15 litres
270 ÷ 9 = 30, so Mrs Conway's car needs 30 lots of ½ a litre of petrol. 30 lots of ½ a litre is 30 ÷ 2 = 15 litres.

22. £25.50
The total distance Roberto travelled is 24 + 15 + 12 = 51 km. In the taxi it costs 25p to travel 500 m, so to travel 1 km would be 2 × 25p = 50p. The total cost would be 51 × 50p = 2550p = £25.50.

23. D
There are 4 kg of meatballs, so twice as much pasta would be 4 × 2 = 8 kg. Altogether there is 4 + 8 = 12 kg of meatballs and pasta. Each serving is 250 g, so 4 servings would be 4 × 250 g = 1000 g = 1 kg. So there are 12 × 4 = 48 servings in 12 kg.

24. 13.5 m
10 mm = 1 cm, so a 15 mm paper clip is 15 ÷ 10 = 1.5 cm long. James used 250 3 cm paper clips, and 400 1.5 cm paper clips. Total length = (250 × 3) + (400 × 1.5) = 750 + 600 = 1350 cm. 1 m = 100 cm, so 1350 ÷ 100 = 3.5 m.

Pages 39-40

1. 3:45, quarter to four or 15:45
The hour hand is pointing between 3 and 4, so the hour is 3. The minute hand is pointing at 9, which is 45 minutes past the hour. So the time is 3:45.

2. E
If the number of hours on a 24-hour clock is between 13 and 23, you can work out the time in the 12-hour clock by subtracting 12 from the number of hours. 19 – 12 = 7, so the time on clock A is 7:20 pm. On clock E the hour hand is pointing between 7 and 8, so the hour is 7. The minute hand is pointing at 4, which is 20 minutes past the hour.

3. D
Twenty to seven in the evening is 6:40 pm. The 12-hour clocks do not show this time because none of them have their hour hand between 6 and 7. On a 24-hour clock, 6 o'clock will be shown by 6 + 12 = 18. One digital clock shows 18:40, which is the same as 6:40 pm. D is the answer.

4.   18:45
Clock A is 35 minutes further ahead than it should be, so you need to subtract 35 minutes from the time shown. Subtract 20 minutes from 19:20 to get to 19:00. Subtract 15 minutes from 19:00 to get to 18:45.

5.   B
There are 60 minutes in an hour, so 90 minutes is 1 hour and 30 minutes. Add 1 hour to ten past 8 and you get ten past 9, add 30 mins to that and you get 9:40. The clock showing 9:40 is B. The hour hand is pointing between 9 and 10, so the hour is 9. The minute hand is pointing to 8, which is 40 minutes past the hour.

6.   25 minutes
The 35 bus leaves the Bus Station at 10:15 and arrives at Bank Street at 10:40. Add 5 minutes to get from 10:15 to 10:20 and add 20 minutes to get from 10:20 to 10:40.
5 + 20 = 25 minutes.

7.   35 minutes
The 42 bus leaves at 11:25 and arrives at Bigsby Road at 12:00. Add 5 minutes to get from 11:25 to 11:30 and add 30 minutes to get from 11:30 to 12:00.
5 + 30 = 35 minutes.

8.   27 minutes
The 35 bus leaves Bank Street at 10:40 and arrives at Clayton Close at 11:07. Add 20 minutes to get from 10:40 to 11:00 and add 7 minutes to get from 11:00 to 11:07.
20 + 7 = 27 minutes.

9.   5 minutes
The 35 bus leaves the Bus Station at 10:15 and arrives at the Hospital at 11:20. So add 1 hour to 10:15 to get to 11:15 and add 5 minutes to get from 11:15 to 11:20.
1 hour = 60 minutes, 60 + 5 = 65 minutes in total. The 42 bus leaves the Bus Station at 11:25 and arrives at the hospital at 12:25. So that means it took 1 hour to complete the journey, which is 60 minutes. So the difference between the times the buses take is 65 – 60 = 5 minutes.

10.   10:13 am
The teacher allowed 12 minutes for the walk and 5 minutes to find their seats. 12 + 5 = 17 minutes, so they must have left 17 minutes before 10:30.
10:30 am – 17 minutes = 10:13 am.

11.   28th July
The closest months to August are October and July. 28th July is less than a month from 15th August, but 4th October is more than a month. So the answer is 28th July.

12.   9th October
You need to count on 12 days after 27th September. There are 30 days in September, so 3 of the days will be in September. 12 – 3 = 9, so that leaves 9 days in October. Mary's birthday will be 9th October.

13.   225
There are 60 seconds in a minute, so 3 x 60 = 180 seconds. Work out $\frac{3}{4}$ of a minute: 60 ÷ 4 = 15, 15 x 3 = 45 seconds. So 3$\frac{3}{4}$ minutes = 180 + 45 = 225 seconds.

14.   E
25 minutes to midnight is 11:35 pm using the 12-hour clock. To find a time after 1 pm on a 24-hour clock you need to add 12 to the hours. So 11 pm would be 11 + 12 = 23. 11:35 pm is 23:35.

15.   95 minutes
Jessica's literacy class starts at 11:10, so you need to subtract 35 minutes from 11:10. Subtract 30 minutes to get to 10:40 and then subtract 5 minutes to get to 10:35. Lunch starts at 12:15 and Jessica returns to school 5 minutes before the start of lunch, so she returns at 12:10. Work out the time difference between 10:35 and 12:10. 10:35 to 11 is 25 minutes. 11 to 12 is 1 hour, so that's 60 minutes. 12 to 12:10 is 10 minutes. 25 + 60 + 10 = 95 minutes.

16.   6 hours and 30 minutes
Mr Smith started at quarter to ten in the morning, which is 9:45 am. Add on 15 minutes to get to 10 am. Add on 7 hours to get to 5 pm. Then add on 15 minutes to get to 5:15 pm. 15 minutes + 7 hours + 15 minutes = 7 hours and 30 minutes. He took 1 hour off for lunch, 7 hours and 30 minutes – 1 hour = 6 hours and 30 minutes.

17.   45 minutes
3 people took swimming lessons, so you need to divide 2 hours and 15 minutes by 3. It is easier to divide this time if it is converted into minutes. 1 hour is 60 minutes, so two hours is 2 x 60 = 120 minutes. 120 + 15 = 135 minutes. 135 ÷ 3 = 45 minutes.

18.   Friday
You know that 18th May is a Tuesday, so every 7th day after 18th May will also be a Tuesday. Add 7 days on at a time to 18th May. Remember, there are 31 days in May.
18th May + 7 days = 25th May.
25th May + 7 days = 1st June.
1st June + 7 days = 8th June.
8th June + 7 days = 15th June.
15th June is a Tuesday, now add on three days to Tuesday to find what day of the week 18th June is. 1st day = Wednesday, 2nd day = Thursday and 3rd day = Friday.

19.   4 hours and 10 minutes
In one week she spends: 25 x 5 = 125 minutes doing her homework. In two weeks she spends:
2 x 125 = 250 minutes. 1 hour = 60 minutes, so 4 hours would be 4 x 60 minutes = 240 minutes. So she would spend 4 hours and 10 minutes doing her homework.

20.   11:35 and 13:55
Javier took 2 hours and 20 minutes, so you need to find the pair of times which has this difference. The answer is 11:35 and 13:55. Add two hours to 11:35 to get to 13:35 and add 20 minutes to get from 13:35 to 13:55.

21.   11:10 am and 1 pm
Molly visited the zoo on a Thursday in February, so the zoo was open between 10:30 am and 3:30 pm. Molly arrived 40 minutes after it opened. Add 30 minutes to get from 10:30 am to 11 am, then add 10 minutes to get from 11 am to 11:10 am. She left 2$\frac{1}{2}$ hours before it closed. Subtract 30 minutes from 3:30 pm to get to 3 pm and subtract 2 hours from 3 pm to get to 1 pm. So Molly was at the zoo between 11:10 am and 1 pm.

Section Seven
— Mixed Problems

Pages 41-42

1. 50%

The black and silver segments make up half of the pie chart. That means that 50% of the people drove black or silver cars.

2. 8

To find how long it will take to eat 40% of the bag you need to work out what $\frac{1}{20}$ is as a percentage. Convert $\frac{1}{20}$ into an equivalent fraction with a denominator of 100. Multiply the numerator and the denominator by 5 to get $\frac{5}{100}$. That means that $\frac{1}{20}$ is the same as 5%. It takes Greg 1 day to eat 5% of the bag, so it takes him $40 \div 5 = 8$ days to eat 40% of the bag.

3. Blueberry

The modal value is the value which is the most common. The pictogram shows more people chose Blueberry pie that any other pie, so it is the modal flavour of pie.

4. 25p

Convert £4.50 into pence by multiplying it by 100, $4.5 \times 100 = 450p$. 9 day's worth of seeds costs 450p, so 1 day's worth of seeds costs $450 \div 9 = 50p$. 2 cups of seeds are used each day, so the cost of 1 cup is $50p \div 2 = 25p$.

5. £198

The area of the hallway is $6 \times 1.5 = 9\,m^2$.
The cost of the carpet is $22 \times 9 = £198$.

6. 2000 l

From 8:20 am to 9 am is 40 minutes. From 9 am to 10 am is 60 minutes. $40 + 60 = 100$ minutes. 20 litres goes into the pool every minute, so $100 \times 20 = 2000$ litres.

7. D

The area of the patio is $8 \times 4 = 32\,m^2$. The area of the each slab is $1 \times 1 = 1\,m^2$. Each slab costs £6.00 and you need 32 to cover the patio. $6 \times 32 = £192$

8. $\frac{1}{4}$

Angles on a straight line add up to $180°$.
So $x = 180° - 75° - 60° = 45°$.
$45° \times 4 = 180°$, so x is $\frac{1}{4}$ of $180°$.

9. £100

If the mean of Mrs Farooq's gas bill is £80, then the total is $4 \times 80 = £320$. Reading off the chart, July's bill = £40, October's bill = £60 and January's bill = £120.
$40 + 60 + 120 = £220$, so the bill in April is
$320 - 220 = £100$.

10. 40 %

Volume = length × width × height. So the volume of the container is $25 \times 10 \times 10 = 2500\,cm^3$. The container is filled with $1000\,cm^3$ of water, so the fraction of the container filled with water is $\frac{1000}{2500} = \frac{10}{25}$. To find this as a percentage you need to turn it into an equivalent fraction with 100 as the denominator. Multiply the numerator and the denominator by 4 to get $\frac{40}{100}$. $\frac{40}{100} = 40\%$.

11. B

If you read off the bar chart the number of German books is 8. There are 40 books in total, so the probability of picking up a German book is $\frac{8}{40}$. This can be simplified to $\frac{1}{5}$ if you divide the numerator and the denominator by 8.

12. 10

Find how much washing liquid is needed per bucket.
1 litre = 1000 ml, so 500 ml is 0.5 litres. In 6 litres there are 12 lots of 0.5 litres ($12 \times 0.5 = 6$). So the total amount of washing liquid in 1 bucket = $12 \times 5\,ml = 60\,ml$. The bottle contains 600 ml of washing liquid, so $600\,ml \div 60\,ml = 10$ buckets.

13. $2H + 4S$

The pattern uses 2 hexagons and 4 squares (which have been cut into 8 triangles). The area of 1 hexagon is H, so the area of 2 hexagons = $2H$. The area of 1 square is S, so the area of 4 squares = $4S$. Altogether the area of Hannah's pattern is $2H + 4S$.

14. $2a + 2b$

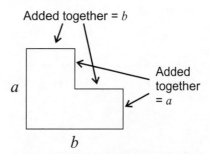

Added together = b

Added together = a

a

b

The two unknown sides opposite to the labelled side a add together to make a. The two unknown sides opposite to the labelled side b add together to make b. So the perimeter is $2a + 2b$.

15. B

Find which rule will give the first number in the sequence. For the first number $n = 1$, only 2 rules will give 5 as an answer. If $n = 1$, $7n - 2 = 7 - 2 = 5$, and $n + 4 = 1 + 4 = 5$. Try these rules for $n = 2$. $7n - 2 = 14 - 2 = 12$, and $n + 4 = 2 + 4 = 6$. Only $7n - 2$ gives the right number for both terms.

16. 310 kg

If the mean weight of the crop from the 5 trees is 320 kg, then the total weight would be $5 \times 320 = 1600$ kg.
The total crop from four trees is,
$370 + 280 + 330 + 310 = 1290$ kg,
The crop from the 5th tree will be, $1600 - 1290 = 310$ kg.

17. £73.50

Gerald is paid £3.50 for every half hour, so he is paid $£3.50 \times 2 = £7.00$ for every hour. Next work out how many hours he works for. From 6:20 am to 4:20 pm is 10 hours. From 4:20 pm to 4:50 pm is 30 minutes, or half an hour. So he worked for a total of 10 and a half hours. He was paid $10 \times £7.00 = £70.00$ for the ten hours, and £3.50 for the half hour. So he earned $£70.00 + £3.50 = £73.50$ in total.

18. 360 ml

From 4 pm on Monday to 4 pm on Tuesday is 24 hours. From 4 pm on Tuesday to 4 pm on Wednesday is 24 hours, but subtract 2 hours to get back to 2 pm. So that's $24 - 2 = 22$ hours. $24 + 22 = 46$ hours. $46 \div 2 = 23$ doses, but this doesn't include her first dose, so the total number of doses = $23 + 1 = 24$ doses. 1 dose = 15 ml, so $24 \times 15 = 360$ ml.

Assessment Test 1

Pages 43-48

1. B
£5 + £2 = £7, 5p + 2p + 1p = 8p. £7 + 8p = £7.08

2. 10:05
The first train after 9 am from Chapel Street is at 9:15.
It arrives in Lanston at 10:05.

3. B
The cake is cut into 8 equal pieces, so each piece is $\frac{1}{8}$.

4. D
The right angled triangle has 1 right angle, the square has 4 right angles. None of the other shapes have any.

5. C
In the 24-hour clock, if the hour is greater than 12 the time is between midday and midnight, which is pm. To convert from the 24-hour clock to the 12-hour clock, subtract 12 from the hour: 16 − 12 = 4. So 16:50 is the same as to 4:50 pm, which is ten to five in the afternoon.

6. (4, 2)
Here is the route she follows:

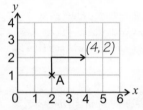

Don't forget — the x-axis coordinate always goes first when you're writing coordinates.

7. C
A, B, D and E can be split into two of the trapezium-shaped tiles shown. C can't because the tiles overlap.

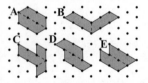

8. 1404
There are 3 lots of 2808 (multiplication is repeated addition), which is equal to 6 lots of something. 6 is double 3, so halve 2808 to find the missing number. Half of 2808 is 1404. So 2808 + 2808 + 2808 = 1404 × 6.

9. £8.91
Round each 99p up to £1 by adding 1p, then multiply by 9: £1 × 9 = £9. You added 9 × 1p to the total cost. So subtract the extra 9p. £9 − 9p = £8.91

10. 5
Work through your 5 times table until you come to first number greater than 24. 5 × 5 = 25, so 5 tents would be enough.

11. D
Read the number of children who chose plums and the number who chose pears off the horizontal axis. Plums = 40, pears = 15. Subtract to find how many more children chose plums than pears: 40 − 15 = 25.

12. 1.07
One way of doing 10 − 8.93 is to count up from 8.93 to 10 on a quick sketch of a number line:

0.07 + 1 = 1.07

13. 61
You can't calculate the blue team total straight away. One method is to calculate the number of points won by the Year 5 blue team first (90 − 27 − 32 = 31). Then use this to find the blue team total (31 + 30 = 61).

Team	Year 5	Year 6	Total
Red	27	50	77
Yellow	32	25	57
Blue	**31**	30	**61**
Total	90	105	

Alternatively, find the grand total by adding the numbers on the bottom row (90 + 105 = 195). Then use this to find the blue team total (195 − 77 − 57 = 61).

14. B
In 45.952, 9 is in the tenths column. Look at the number in the next column to the right (the hundredths). It is 5, so round the 9 tenths up to 10 tenths. 10 tenths is one unit, so the rounded number is 46.0.

15. B
The whole circle represents 36 children. The yellow area of the pie chart is a quarter of the circle. $\frac{1}{4}$ of 36 is 36 ÷ 4 = 9. 9 children wore yellow hats.

16. 8.1 l
Add up the three volumes:

$$\begin{array}{r} 4.4 \\ 0.9 \\ + 2.8 \\ \hline 8.1 \\ {\scriptstyle 2} \end{array}$$

17. D
Imagine folding the net up to make a cuboid. Corner D will touch X.

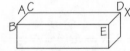

18. 36.6 g
$\frac{1}{4}$ tin has 12.2 g of carbohydrate. $\frac{3}{4}$ is 3 times as much as $\frac{1}{4}$, so 12.2 g × 3 = 36.6 g of carbohydrate.

19. 6p
10% of 40p is 40 ÷ 10 = 4p. So the cost of each packet is 40 − 4 = 36p. There are 6 bears in each packet, so the cost of each bear is 36 ÷ 6 = 6p.

20. D
The spinner can be split into 10 equal sections. 6 out of the 10 sections are spotty, so the probability of the spinner landing on a spotty section is $\frac{6}{10}$ or $\frac{3}{5}$. This means that more than half of the segments are spotty, so there is more chance of the spinner landing on a spotty section than any other section.

21.　A

You need to use BODMAS to work out each option.
A: 8 × 3 = 24, 48 −24 = 24 — A is the correct answer.
B: 11 × 2 = 22, 3 + 22 = 25.
C: 3 × 7 = 21
D: 24 ÷ 2 = 12, 12 − 1 = 11
E: 4 × 4 = 16, 2 + 16 = 18

22.　D

Scalene triangles have three different sides and three different angles. Rhombuses, kites, regular pentagons and isosceles triangles have at least two equal sides and two equal angles.

23.　E

Multiples of 100 are divisible by 4 (100 ÷ 4 = 25), so ignore the number in the hundreds column and see if the rest of the number is divisible by 4.
A: 324 so 24 ÷ 4 = 6
B: 116 so 16 ÷ 4 = 4
C: 288 so 88 ÷ 4 = 22
D: 132 so 32 ÷ 4 = 8
E: 138 so 38 ÷ 4 = 9 r 2. So E is the answer.

24.　0.9 kg

First calculate the mass of the 7 peaches:
7 × 200 g = 1400 g. 1 kg = 1000 g, so 1400 g = 1.4 kg.
The mass of the basket: 2.3 − 1.4 = 0.9 kg.

25.　6

Write the sizes out in order: 4, 5, 5, 6, 6, 6, 7, 7, 8
The median is the middle value. There are 9 numbers, so the median is the 5th number in the list, 6.

26.　C

Angle y is bigger than a right angle (90°), so it can't be 60° (B) or 90° (D). It is smaller than a straight line (180°), so it can't be 180° (A). 175° (E) is almost a straight line and angle y is smaller than a straight line by more than 5°. So that leaves C as the only possible answer.

27.　B

Look at the points on the graph and see which child has a gap of 2 points between their two scores. Peter is the only child with a difference of 2 points. If you read off the graph, his scores are 9 and 7.

28.　25.5

There are 10 spaces between 24 and 26. So each space is worth 2 ÷ 10 = 0.2. The arrow is pointing half way between 25.4 and 25.6. Half of the gap between 25.4 and 25.6 is 0.2 ÷ 2 = 0.1, so the number the arrow is pointing to is 25.4 + 0.1 = 25.5.

29.　48 m²

The area of a triangle is ½ × base × height. The playground is made up of four identical triangles. The area of one of them is ½ × 6 × 4 = 12 m². So the area of the whole playground is 12 × 4 = 48 m².

30.　32

To find the answer you need to work backwards from 131. You're told that a number was divided by 2 to make 131 — so the number was 131 × 2 = 262. You're told that 6 was added to a number to make 262, so subtract 6 from 262, 262 − 6 = 256. You're told that a number was multiplied by 8 to make 256, so divide 256 by 8. 256 ÷ 8 = 32.

31.　B

The angles, corners and the lines of symmetry are marked on the shape below (a right angle = 90°).

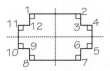

The shape has eight internal 90° angles, not four.
So B is incorrect.

32.　Croc Chase

On the graph, you can see that the February sales are lowest. The only game for which this is true is Croc Chase.

33.　£15

If Amanda spent 60% of her pocket money, she must have 40% left. 40% = £6.00, so 10% would be £6 ÷ 4 = £1.50. So 100% would be 10 × £1.50 = £15.

34.　28 cm

The length of each side of the hexagon is 2 cm. The outer edge of the shape is made up of 14 hexagon sides. So the total length = 2 × 14 = 28 cm

35.　50 mins

Divide 1 litre by 20 ml to see how many minutes it will take. 1 litre = 1000 ml. So you need to work out 1000 ÷ 20. You can make this easier to work out by dividing both numbers by 10, so that's 100 ÷ 2 = 50 mins.

36.　−8 °C

The temperature drops from 1 °C to −2 °C, which is a drop of 3 °C, from Tuesday to Wednesday. Twice this is 3 °C × 2 = 6 °C. 6 °C lower than −2 °C is −8 °C.

37.　500 g

The ingredients given make 12 cakes.
40 cakes = 3 lots of 12 cakes + 4 cakes.
4 cakes = ⅓ of 12 cakes. She will need to multiply the amount of butter given by 3⅓. You can partition 3⅓ into 3 + ⅓.
⅓ × 150 g = 150 ÷ 3 = 50 g. 150 g × 3 = 450 g.
So the total amount of butter is 450 g + 50 g = 500 g

38.　D

Look at the top right corner of the rectangle, and follow the instructions to see where it would move to.

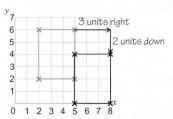

The top right corner would now be at point (8, 4). This coordinate is only in option D, so that's the answer.

39.　A

The only days on which there is a meat pie and a non-apple dessert are Monday and Friday. This is two days out of five, so the probability is ⅖.

40.   152 cm³

Volume of cube = length × width × height. You're not given the height for the cube, but it must be 4 cm, because the length, width and height of a cube are all equal.
So the volume = 4 cm × 4 cm × 4 cm = 64 cm³
Volume of cuboid = length × width × height.
The width of the cuboid is equal to the width of the cube, so the volume = 5.5 cm × 4 cm × 4 cm = 88 cm³
Total = 64 cm³ + 88 cm³ = 152 cm³

41.   E

The numbers increase by 5 each time. This means that the sequence is related to the 5 times table, and 5n will be in the nth term expression. The first term is 3, so when n = 1, the expression must give 3. So it must be 5n – 2, because 5 × 1 – 2 = 3.

42.   E

The mean of a set of four numbers is the total of the numbers divided by 4. So if the mean is 4, the total of the numbers is 4 × 4 = 16. The two sides you can see add up to 11 (3 + 8). So the two hidden sides must add up to 16 – 11 = 5. The only pair of numbers in the answer choices that add up to 5 is 1 and 4.

43.   375 g

First find out how many 2ps make up £1. £1 = 100p, so there are 100 ÷ 2 = 50 coins in each pile. So each pile should weigh 50 × 7.5 = 375 g.

44.   (7, 6)

The shape is a parallelogram, so the top edge is the same length as the bottom edge. The length of the bottom edge can be found by subtracting the x-coordinate of one end from the x-coordinate of the other end: 5 – 2 = 3 units. So the top edge is also 3 units long. This means that point T's x-coordinate is 4 + 3 = 7. Point T's y-coordinate is 6, because it has the same y-coordinate as point (4, 6).

45.   11:05 am

If Kate travels at 60 km/h, she will cover 2 × 60 = 120 km in 2 hours. She then goes a further 15 km (135 – 120). 15 km is ¼ of 60 km, so she will travel 15 km in ¼ of an hour. She travels for 2¼ hours in total. If she starts at 8:50 am, she will arrive at 11:05 am.

46.   C

The amount of discount received off the original price of £27.50 was £27.50 – £24.75 = £2.75. Divide the original amount by the discounted price. 27.50 ÷ 2.75 = 10.

47.   C

The different sizes of the symbols makes this graph misleading, e.g. the line of hamsters is the shortest on the pictogram, but they're the most popular pet.

48.   £17.40

Bella gets 6 boxes of 20 cards for 4 × £3.90. Partition £3.90 into £3 + 90p. 4 × £3 = £12, 4 × 90p = £3.60 £12 + £3.60 = £15.60. She also gets 12 cards for £1.80. Total cost = £15.60 + £1.80 = £17.40.

49.   67°

Put 46° into the formula. m = (180 – 46) ÷ 2. m = 134 ÷ 2 = 67°.

50.   B

The customer is charged £50 for the job, plus the number of hours (h) multiplied by £25. So the cost = 50 + 25 × h, or 50 + 25h.

Assessment Test 2

Pages 49-54

1.   D

There are 8 segments and 3 are shaded. This is the fraction ⅜.

2.   A

A small can of beans weighs around 250 g. All of the other weights are either too small or too large.

3.   A

You can work out the area of a rectangle by length × width. So, the area of the flag is 6 × 4 = 24 cm². The flag is split into 4 equal rectangles, so the area of the shaded rectangle is 24 ÷ 4 = 6 cm².

4.   34 minutes

The range is the difference between the fastest time and the slowest time. The fastest time was 156 minutes and the slowest time was 122 minutes. 156 – 122 = 34.

5.   B

You need to find the piece that is the right size to fit in the gap. Shape B has been rotated by 180° but is the only shape that can fit in the gap.

6.   (–1, 2)

Four squares north takes Adam to (–3, 2). Two squares east takes him to his finishing point at (–1, 2).

7.   B

21² is 21 × 21. You can estimate the answer by rounding the numbers to the nearest 10 and working out 20 × 20. 20 × 20 = 400. The only realistic option is B — 441.

8.   C

When you rotate the clear pentagon by 180° it looks like this:

When this is placed on top of the shaded pentagon you will get the shape shown by option C.

9.   A

The difference between 45.6 and 45.9 is 45.9 – 45.6 = 0.3. 0.3 ÷ 2 = 0.15 so the halfway point between the two numbers will be 45.6 + 0.15 = 45.75.

10.   6

Dogs have 2½ symbols and fish have 1 symbol so the difference between them is 1½ symbols. Each symbol in the pictogram is equal to 4 people. So, half of a symbol is 4 ÷ 2 = 2 people. 1½ symbols is equal to 4 people + 2 people = 6 people.

11.   D

90 can be divided by 2 because 90 is an even number. The digits in 90 add up to a multiple of 3 (9 + 0 = 9) so it can be divided by 3. If a number ends in a 5 or 0 it can be divided by 5, so 90 can be divided by 5. 9 × 10 = 90 so 90 can be divided by 9. That leaves 7 — 90 can't be divided by 7.

12.   3 pm

The graph shows a rise in temperature until 3 pm when it starts to drop again. This is when he went outside and left the door open.

13.   C

Add the prices of the sets of three board games together. You need to find the option that adds up to £29.50 (£30.00 – £0.50 = £29.50). This is easiest if you split the numbers and add the pounds and pence separately. £12.50 (Blocks) + £6.50 (Clueless) + £10.50 (Trivia Time) = (£12 + £10 + £6) + (£0.50 + £0.50 + £0.50) = £28 + £1.50 = £29.50.

14.   B

For B, the dial is split into 8 parts and 1 kg is at the 4th point, halfway round the scale. This means that each point on the scale represents 1 kg ÷ 4 = 250 g. As the arrow is pointing at the 3rd point, it is pointing at 3 × 250 g = 750 g.

15.   E

The number 26 is an even number, but it isn't a multiple of 3 or a multiple of 7, so it can't be placed in the sorting table.

16.   68%

To find a percentage you need to get a fraction out of 100. $^{16}/_{50}$ people had a blue car and when you multiply the numerator and denominator in $^{16}/_{50}$ by 2 you get $^{32}/_{100}$. $^{32}/_{100}$ = 32%. The percentage of people who didn't have a blue car is 100 – 32 = 68%.

17.   A

When you multiply two odd numbers together you always make an odd number. So, 113 × 115 will give an odd number as the answer.

18.   C

To find the length of 20 scarves you need to multiply 45 cm by 20. 45 × 20 = 900 cm. There are 100 cm in 1 m, so 900 cm = 9 m.

19.   9

Ester won 32 prizes altogether so subtract the number she won on the other days from 32 to find the number she won on Thursday: 32 – 5 – 4 – 8 – 6 = 9.

20.   25%

The total amount of paint used by Harry is 3 + 4 + 5 = 12 litres. 3 litres of this was red paint, so the fraction of red paint used is $^3/_{12}$. $^3/_{12}$ is simplified to $^1/_4$ by dividing the numerator and denominator by 3, and $^1/_4$ = 25% (25% × 4 = 100%).

21.   120°

Each angle in an equilateral triangle is 60°. The shaded angle is made up of the angles from two equilateral triangles so it is 60 + 60 = 120°.

22.   C

Round up 49p to 50p and 29p to 30p to make the calculations easier. Carrie bought 4 chocolate bars so the approximate price of these is 4 × 50p = £2. She bought 7 bags of peanuts so the approximate price of these is 7 × 30p = £2.10. £2 + £2.10 = £4.10. You rounded each item up by 1p and there were 11 items in total (4 + 7 = 11) so subtract 11p to find the exact total cost: £4.10 – 11p = £3.99.

23.   Red

The mode is the most popular result. Silver, purple and blue each got one vote, gold and green both got two votes but red got three votes, so red is the mode.

24.   50 cm²

The area of each square is length × width = 4 × 4 = 16 cm². The area of $^1/_2$ a square = 16 ÷ 2 = 8 cm². 1 whole square + 3 halves = 16 + 8 + 8 + 8 = 40 cm². She uses $^1/_2$ of a circle for the base and $^1/_2$ of a circle for the nose, so 1 circle in total. The total area of the circle is 10 cm². So, the total area is 40 + 10 = 50 cm².

25.   B

Elsa has 7 + 8 + 3 = 18 sweets to start with. She eats 2 chocolate drops so there are 16 sweets left (18 – 2 = 16). There are still 8 toffees left, so the probability of picking a toffee next is $^8/_{16}$. $^8/_{16}$ = $^1/_2$.

26.   D

Work out the length of time that the journey takes on each bus. On Bus A the journey takes 9:44 to 10:44 = 60 minutes plus 10:44 to 10:56 = 12 minutes. 60 + 12 = 72 minutes. On Bus B the journey takes 11:39 to 12:39 = 60 minutes plus 12:39 to 12:48 = 9 minutes. 60 + 9 = 69 minutes. The journey on Bus A is longer, so the longest time is 72 minutes.

27.   10 years

The plant needs to grow 0.5 m (2 – 1.5 = 0.5). It grows 0.025 m in 6 months. There are 12 months in a year so it will grow 0.025 × 2 = 0.05 m in a year. 0.5 m ÷ 0.05 m = 10, so it'll take the plant 10 years to grow 0.5 m.

28.   E

The y-axis is the vertical axis so the coordinates of the reflected point A are (2, 2) (see the diagram).

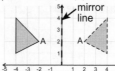

29.   B

3 × 44 = 132 which is an even number so option B is incorrect. All of the other statements are true.

30.   30

	Girls	Boys	Total
Goals		4	
Saves	14	= (20 – 4) = 16	= (16 + 14) = **30**
Total	24	= (44 – 24) = 20	44

The table shows how to find the total number of saves. Start by working out the boys' total goals and saves (20). Then use this to find the number of the boys' saves (16). Add this to the girls' saves to find the total number of saves (30).

31.   D

25 × 4 = 100, so it takes 4 days to run 100 miles. The number of days to run 800 miles will be 4 × 8 = 32 days. This leaves 74 miles left over. 25 × 3 = 75 so it'll take 3 days to complete the last 74 miles. 32 days + 3 days = 35 days.

32.   136°

A kite is a quadrilateral so the angles in a kite add up 360°. This means that the angle next to angle a is 360 – 130 – 130 – 56 = 44°. Angles on a straight line add up to 180°, so angle a is 180 – 44 = 136°.

33.   D

46 is 23 doubled, so 46 × 14 will be 23 × 14 doubled. So 46 × 14 = 322 × 2 = 644. 140 is 10 times larger than 14, so 46 × 140 = 644 × 10 = 6440.

34. £16.00

The cost of tickets for 2 adults and 2 children is £3.50 + £3.50 + £1.50 + £1.50 = £10.00. A family ticket is 20% cheaper — 10% of £10 is £1 so 20% is £2. So a family ticket is £10 – £2 = £8. Raj is buying two family tickets so the total cost is 8 × 2 = £16.

35. D

Look at each statement and decide if it's true:
A: $\frac{3}{4} = \frac{75}{100}$, so $\frac{7}{100}$ is not greater than $\frac{3}{4}$.
B: $\frac{7}{100} = 0.07$, so $\frac{7}{100}$ is not greater than 0.65.
C: $\frac{7}{100} = 0.07$, so $\frac{7}{100}$ is not greater than 0.09.
D: $\frac{3}{4} = 0.75$, so 0.65 is less than $\frac{3}{4}$.
E: 0.65 is greater than 0.09.

36. B

There are two skirts and one of them is white. Mrs Breen picks one skirt, so the probability of picking a white skirt is 1 out of 2 or $\frac{1}{2}$. All of the other statements are incorrect.

37. 160

The number of matchboxes that can fit along the length of the packing box is 10 ÷ 2 = 5. The number that can fit across the width is 8 ÷ 2 = 4 and the number that can fit up the height is 8 ÷ 1 = 8. So, the total number of matchboxes that can fit in the packing box is 5 × 4 × 8 = 20 × 8 = 160.

38. B

Start by making sure everything is in the same units — there were 4 litres of water, so change this to millilitres by multiplying by 1000: 4 × 1000 = 4000 ml. There are 5 holes each losing 80 ml each hour, so the amount of water being lost each hour is 5 × 80 = 400 ml. Divide the total volume of water (4000) by the amount being lost each hour (400) to find the number of hours it'll take to empty: 4000 ÷ 400 = 10 hours.

39. 6.5 m

The vertical sides of the shape measure 1 + 3 + 4 = 8 m. So, the total of the horizontal sides of the shape is 21 – 8 = 13 m. As the shape is a rectangle, the bottom side is half of this, so the length of X (the bottom) is 13 ÷ 2 = 6.5 m.

40. B

n is the number of the term. To find the first term, substitute 1 for n (remember to follow BODMAS): $3 \times 1^2 + 1 = 3 \times 1 + 1 = 3 + 1 = 4$. To find the second term, n is 2: $3 \times 2^2 + 1 = 3 \times 4 + 1 = 12 + 1 = 13$.

41. (3, -3)

The diagram shows the flag when it has been rotated clockwise by 90° about (0, 0). The coordinates of point P are now (3, -3).

42. 12 cm³

The volume of each cube of cheese is $2 \times 2 \times 2 = 8\ cm^3$. There are 3 cubes of cheese, so the total volume of cheese is $8 \times 3 = 24\ cm^3$. The mouse eats $12\ cm^3$ of cheese, so the amount left is $24 - 12 = 12\ cm^3$.

43. B

The cactus plants come in boxes of 12 and Lemone needs 60 plants so she needs 60 ÷ 12 = 5 boxes. The cost of 5 boxes is shown in the expression as 5C. She needs to add this to the cost of the stall, S, so the complete expression is S + 5C.

44. 2

The total angle around the point at the centre of the spinner is 360° and there are 8 segments, so the size of each segment is 360 ÷ 8 = 45°. 360 – 45 = 315° so the arrow is being turned in an anti-clockwise direction through 7 segments (8 – 1 = 7) which will leave it pointing at number 2.

45. D

n is the number of the term. Test each formula by substituting n with at least 3 different values. E.g for option D: n – (n + 1):
When n is 1: 1 – (1 + 1) = 1 – 2 = -1.
When n is 2: 2 – (2 + 1) = 2 – 3 = -1.
When n is 3: 3 – (3 + 1) = 3 – 4 = -1.
So n – (n + 1) is the correct formula.

46. 91

£2.73 is made up evenly of 2p and 1p coins. 1p out of every 3p is a 1p coin, so $\frac{1}{3}$ of the coins are 1p coins. £2.73 is 273p and $\frac{1}{3}$ of 273 is 273 ÷ 3 = 91. So, 91 coins are 1p coins.

47. D

The regular pentagon has 5 sides that are all 2x – y.
$5(2x - y) = 2x - y + 2x - y + 2x - y + 2x - y + 2x - y = 10x - 5y$.

48. 5

The number of sausage rolls eaten by the children is 22 × 3 = 66 and the number eaten by the adults is 7 × 5 = 35. So the total number of sausage rolls eaten is 66 + 35 = 101. The sausage rolls come in packets of 25. 4 × 25 = 100 so Sherrie will need to buy 5 packets to have 101 sausage rolls.

49. B

The area of each tile is $0.04\ m^2$ and Moses uses 100 tiles to cover the floor, so the total area of the bathroom is $100 \times 0.04 = 4\ m^2$. The area of the bathroom is calculated using length × width, so area ÷ width = length: 4 ÷ 1 = 4 m.

50. D

3(x + 6y) means: x + 6y + x + 6y + x + 6y = 3x + 18y.

Assessment Test 3

Pages 55-60

1. 6.5 cm²

The area of a whole square is $1\ cm^2$, so the area of half a square is $0.5\ cm^2$. There are 5 whole squares with an area of $5 \times 1\ cm^2 = 5\ cm^2$, and 3 half squares with an area of $3 \times 0.5\ cm^2 = 1.5\ cm^2$, so the total area is $5 + 1.5 = 6.5\ cm^2$.

2. B

There are two lines of symmetry:

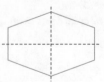

3. C

Litres is not a unit of length. Centimetres and millimetres are too small. Kilometres are too big. So metres is the most suitable unit.

4. 7

Each rectangle represents 4 vehicles, so ¼ of a rectangle represents 1 vehicle. There are 1¾ rectangles for the buses. This is equivalent to 4 buses for the whole rectangle and 3 buses for the ¾ rectangle. 3 + 4 = 7 buses.

5. 6

The children with a skateboard and a scooter are shown in the overlap of the skateboard and scooter circles. The 1 child in the middle section also has a bike, so you don't want to count that one.

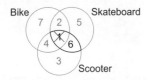

6. C

Total up the 3 items Maddy chose and subtract the total from £5.00. 40p + 25p + 99p = £1.64 (to add on 99p, add on £1 and subtract 1p) £5.00 − £1.64 = £3.36.

7. A

To convert from the 24-hour clock to the 12-hour clock subtract 12 from the hours, in this case, 13. 13 − 12 = 1. In the 24 hour clock, if the number of hours is greater than 12, the time is pm. So the answer is 1:45 pm.

8. 6:05 pm

1¾ hours = 1 hour 45 mins. Count on 1 hour and 45 mins from 4:20 pm. One hour later than 4:20 pm is 5:20 pm, 40 minutes later than 5:20 pm is 6:00 pm, 5 minutes later than 6:00 pm is 6:05 pm. Alternatively, 1¾ hours is 15 minutes less than 2 hours. So you could add on 2 hours and then subtract 15 minutes.

9. D

It is difficult to divide 9.45 by 1.5, so round it down to 9. There are 6 × 1.5 in 9, so the answer must be about 6 — D is the only possible answer.

10. B

400 g is the only sensible answer. 4 kg and 40 kg are too big. 4 g and 0.4 g are too small.

11. 113

Add up the number of boys and girls in each year group.
Year 3:   49 + 50 = 99
Year 4:   52 + 56 = 108
Year 5:   55 + 57 = 112
Year 6:   54 + 59 = 113
Year 7:   10 + 20 = 30
Year 6 is the biggest year group and has 113 children.

12. 26

A cube has 6 faces, 12 edges and 8 vertices (corners). 6 + 12 + 8 = 26. If you don't know these, you could count them on the diagram in the question.

13. 7.2

0.08 is 1000 times smaller than 80, so 90 × 0.08 will be 1000 times smaller than 90 × 80. 90 × 80 = 7200, so 90 × 0.08 = 7200 ÷ 1000 = 7.2

14. 11

1.75 pints = 1 litre, so 6 litres = 1.75 pints × 6. Split the calculation up to make it easier. 2 litres = 2 × 1.75 = 3.5 pints. 6 litres = 3 × 2 litres, so 6 litres = 3.5 × 3 = 10.5 pints. So you'd need 11 bottles.

15. E

E (a trapezium) is the only shape with one pair of parallel sides (the top and bottom). A and D have more than one pair of parallel sides. B and C have no parallel sides.

16. B

The pattern is made up of a set of three shapes that repeat. 3 × 6 = 18, so there will be 6 full sets of the shapes, plus another two that make up the first 20 shapes. The heart is the 1st shape in the pattern, so shape 19 will be a heart. So there will be 6 + 1 = 7 hearts.

17. Ian

The fastest time is the smallest number. Cara was fastest with a time of 3 mins 59 secs. Ian came second with a time of 4 mins 2 secs.

18. B

Ian has rounded each item up by 1p. There are 9 items, so his estimate will be 9p too much.

19. E

42 is half of 84, so 349 × 42 will be half of 29 316. 29 316 is just under 30 000, so the answer should be just under half of this, around 15 000. Option E is the only possible option.

20. D

The numbers above 4 on a dice are 5 and 6. This is 2 out of the 6 numbers, so the probability is ²⁄₆ = ⅓.

21. B

Convert all the fractions to twentieths so they're easier to put in order: ¾ = ¹⁵⁄₂₀ (Multiply the numerator and denominator by 5.) ⅕ = ⁴⁄₂₀ (Multiply the numerator and denominator by 4.) The other three fractions are already in twentieths. In order from smallest to largest, the fractions are: ³⁄₂₀, ⁴⁄₂₀, ⁵⁄₂₀, ⁷⁄₂₀, ¹⁵⁄₂₀. Convert the fractions back to their original form to give: ³⁄₂₀, ⅕, ⁵⁄₂₀, ⁷⁄₂₀, ¾.

22. 2.5 °C

The highest temperature was 38.5 °C on Saturday. The lowest temperature was 36 °C on Monday and Wednesday. So the range = 38.5 − 36 = 2.5 °C.

23. 597 miles

If Sue can travel 2985 miles on 5 tanks, she can travel 2985 ÷ 5 miles on 1 tank:

$$\begin{array}{r} 5\ \ 9\ \ 7 \\ 5\overline{)2\ 9\ ^48\ ^35} \end{array}$$

24. E

The map below shows Jenny's movements. Remember — 90° is a right angle, so 135° is one and a half right angles (90° + 45°).

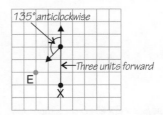

25. 6

Two different numbers are multiplied by 56, then added together to make 560. 560 is the same as 56 × 10. You already know that part of the calculation is 4 × 56, so to get 560 the other part must be 6 × 56 (6 + 4 = 10). (4 × 56) + (6 × 56) = 10 × 56 = 560.

26.   E

You need to imagine spinning the shape round to different positions. This question is easier if you rotate the page so that the cube with the heart is at the top each time.

27.   11

To find the answer you need to work backwards from 112. You're told that 9 was subtracted from a number to make 112 — which must mean that the number was 121 (112 + 9 = 121). To reach 121 the original number was multiplied by 11. So you need to divide 121 by 11 to find the original number: 121 ÷ 11 = 11.

28.   14

To calculate the mean, add all numbers together and divide by the number of classes (6).
Mean = (16 + 16 + 11 + 17 + 12 + 12) ÷ 6 = 84 ÷ 6 = 14

29.   52 m²

First find the area of the whole garden, then subtract the area of the flower bed. This gives you the lawn area.
Garden = 8 × 8 = 64 m²
Flower bed = 4 × 3 = 12 m²
Lawn = 64 – 12 = 52 m²

30.   E

Count up from –5 in steps of 1.5 until you land on one of the answer choices. –5, –3.5, –2, –0.5, 1, 2.5, 4 (which is E)

31.   12

From the chart, you can see that 70% of children in the computer club are boys. There are 30 children in the club, so find 70% of 30. 10% of 30 = 30 ÷ 10 = 3 so 70% = 7 × 10% = 7 × 3 = 21. There must be 30 – 21 = 9 girls. So there are 21 – 9 = 12 more boys than girls.

32.   2 km

Sarah runs on 7 × 12 = 84 days
Each day she runs 168 ÷ 84 = 2 km.

33.   D

There are seven days in one week. Count on six lots of seven from 23rd April. There are 30 days in April and 31 in May.
30th April, 7th May, 14th May, 21st May, 28th May, 4th June.

34.   210

The calculation is easier if you recognise that
11 + 12 + 13 + 14 + 15 + 16 + 17 + 18 + 19 + 20 is the same as (1 + 2 + 3 + 4 + 5 + 6 + 7 + 8 + 9 + 10) + (10 × 10).
So the total = 55 + 55 + 100 = 210

35.   31

You could do this question by predicting what the 11th shape will look like and counting the squares. Shape 11 will have a vertical strip of 11 squares, and the horizontal strips sticking out the sides will be 10 squares long each. The total number of squares will be 11 + 10 + 10 = 31. Alternatively, you could say that the number of squares increases by 3 each time. There are 10 squares in Shape 4, and Shape 11 is 7 shapes further on. So Shape 11 will have 7 × 3 = 21 more squares than Shape 4. This means it has 10 + 21 = 31 in total.

36.   B

There are 1000 ml in 1 litre, so in 10 litres, there are 10 000 ml. ⅖ of a litre = ⅖ × 1000 ml = (1000 × 2) ÷ 5 = 2000 ÷ 5 = 400 ml. So the amount left in the bucket = 10 000 – 400 = 9600 ml

37.   B

Consider whether each statement is true:
A: There are 4 even numbers and only 2 odd, so this isn't true.
B: 3 numbers out of 6 are greater than 4, so the probability of it landing on one of them is even. The statement is true.
C: There are 6 equal sections, and so each number has a one-sixth chance of being spun. So the statement isn't true.
D: More than half the numbers are even, so the probability of an even number being spun can't be one-third. So the statement isn't true.
E: There are only two numbers less than 3. This is less than half of the possible numbers, so the probability of one of them being spun can't be a half.

38.   (8, 2)

Point T is directly below the point (8, 10) so it will have the same x-coordinate (8). Point T is directly to the right of the point (4, 2) so it will have the same y-coordinate (2). So, the coordinates of point T are (8, 2).

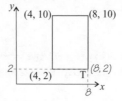

39.   2016

Find the total number of seats (42 × 48):

```
      48
  ×   42
    1920
        3
  +   96
      1
    2016
    11
```

40.   30 cm³

The area of the triangular side = ½ × base × height = ½ × 3 × 2 = 3 cm². Volume = area of triangular side × length = 3 × 10 = 30 cm³

41.   B

Add the numbers together and divide by 2 to find the value half way between them. 4.19 + 3.81 = 8. 8 ÷ 2 = 4.

42.   48 cm

The perimeter of a rectangle is made up of 2 lengths and 2 widths. So 1 length + 1 width = half the perimeter = 128 ÷ 2 = 64 cm. The length is 3 times as long as the width so the width × 4 = 64 cm. So the width is 64 ÷ 4 = 16 cm. Multiply the width by 3 to find the length: 16 × 3 = 48cm.

43.   3

Read off how many °C is the same as 25 °F from the graph — it's approximately –4 °C. The table tells you that the minimum temperature for a sleeping bag with rating 3 is –5 °C. This is the lowest rated sleeping bag he can get.

44.   C

Write out the four given ages in order: 2, 3, 6, 8. For the median age to stay the same, 3 and 6 have to remain the middle two values. So one of the missing ages must be 3 or less, and the other must be 6 or more. This means that the correct answer must be C — 2 and 8.

45.   B

The minute hand will go round 10.5 times between 12 noon and 10:30 pm. It travels through 360° each time it goes round. So the total angle it travels through is 10.5 × 360° = 3780°.

46.   **(2, –2)**

The reflected point is the same distance away from the mirror line on both sides.

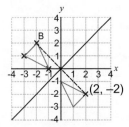

47.   **£50**

Substitute 300 for *m* in the formula and find C. Remember to follow BODMAS.

$C = 15(300 ÷ 100) + 5$
$C = 15(3) + 5$
$C = 45 + 5$
$C = 50$

The cost of printing 300 leaflets is £50.

48.   **B**

The whole pie chart represents 20 days. If 20 days = 360°, then 1 day = 360 ÷ 20 = 18°. 3 foggy days will be represented by an angle of 3 × 18° = 54°.

49.   **£9.75**

Find 30% of £2.50: 10% of £2.50 = £0.25
30% = 3 × 10% = £0.25 × 3 = £0.75.
So if he cleans the car one week he gets £2.50 + £0.75 = £3.25
If he does this for 3 weeks, he gets £3.25 × 3 = £9.75

50.   **D**

1 game costs £39.99, so n games will cost him
n × 39.99 = 39.99n. The computer cost £260.
Subtract these amounts from £500 to find what he has left over: 500 – 260 – 39.99n = 240 – 39.99n

Assessment Test 4

Pages 61-66

1.   **E**

1 million is 1 000 000, so 7 000 000 is seven million.

2.   **A**

Trees are usually taller than a person's height. The other measurements are all much smaller than a person's height.

3.   **D**

A shape with six sides is formed, which is a hexagon.

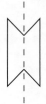

4.   **Monday**

−2°C is the lowest temperature in the table.

5.   **1 hour 20 mins**

The programme starts at 6:55 pm and finishes at 8:15 pm.
Count on 1 hour from 6:55 pm to 7:55 pm. Then count on from 7:55 pm to 8:15 pm which is 20 more minutes, making a total of 1 hour 20 minutes.

6.   **17.5 cm²**

The area of a rectangle is length × width. So, the area is 7 × 2.5.
Partition 2.5 into 2 and 0.5 and multiply each number by 7.
7 × 2 = 14. 7 × 0.5 = 3.5. So 7 × 2.5 = 14 + 3.5 = 17.5 cm².

7.   **0.18**

Only two of the numbers are less than 1: 0.81 and 0.18.
0.18 only has 1 tenth, whereas 0.81 has 8 tenths.
So 0.18 is smallest.

8.   **E**

She starts at (4, 3) so one unit east takes her to (5, 3).
Two units south take her to (5, 1). So, she ends up at point E.

9.   **8:30 am**

The latest bus arriving at Rippen before 8:40 am is the one that leaves Kneesall (where Lucas lives) at 8:30 am.

10.   **41**

The frequency just shows how many times each number has been rolled. Read off the frequency of each number and add them up to find out how many times the dice was thrown altogether:
6 + 7 + 8 + 5 + 9 + 6 = 41.

11.   **B**

You can find the answer by rounding the prices of the bunches of flowers. The cost of three bunches at £1.49, is slightly less than £1.50 × 3 = £4.50. The other bunch costs £1.99, which rounds to £2. So the total cost is about £4.50 + £2 = £6.50. You've rounded up each time, so the actual cost will be slightly less than £6.50, so answer B (£6.46) is the only possible choice.

12.   **E**

Compare the angle to a right angle.
It is approximately half of a right angle. 90° ÷ 2 = 45°.

13.   **C**

There are 8 spaces on the scale between 0 and 4 kg. So each space is worth 4 ÷ 8 = 0.5 kg. The arrow is half a space further along than 2 kg on the scale. Half of 0.5 kg = 0.25 kg. So the kitten weighs 2 kg + 0.25 kg = 2.25 kg

14.   **8 cm**

Regular heptagons have seven equal sides, so each side is
56 ÷ 7 = 8 cm.

15.   **3.750 kg**

First find the mass of each type of fruit:
Oranges: 600 × 1 = 600 g
Bananas: 450 × 2 = 900 g
Apples: 500 × 3 = 1500 g
Pears: 750 × 1 = 750 g
Add up all the masses:
600 + 900 = 1500 g
1500 + 1500 = 3000 g
3000 + 750 = 3750 g
Convert the grams to kilograms:
1000 g = 1 kg, so 3750 g = 3.750 kg

16.   **B**

If he had one loaf and ate an equal amount each day, he'd eat $\frac{1}{7}$ of a loaf. He has three loaves, so he eats three times more each day.
$3 × \frac{1}{7} = \frac{3}{7}$.

17.   **E**

The dogs' area of the pie chart is slightly bigger than a quarter of the chart. Calculate a quarter of the 32 pets: 32 ÷ 4 = 8.
9 is one more than 8. The other choices are too big or too small to be reasonable estimates.

18.   B

9 is greater than 5, so 39 rounds up to 40. 3 is less than 5, so 43 rounds down to 40. 40 x 40 = 1600.

19.   35

Find the number of groups by dividing the number of girls in the class by the number of girls in a group: 15 ÷ 3 = 5 groups. The number of children in a group is 4 + 3 = 7, so the total number of children = 5 x 7 = 35. Alternatively, find the number of boys in the class by multiplying the number of boys in a group by the number of groups:
4 x 5 = 20 boys. 15 girls + 20 boys = 35 children in total

20.   D

Convert prices in £ to pence, then divide the price by the number of cakes.
A   15p each
B   39p ÷ 3 = 13p each
C   100p ÷ 10 = 10p each
D   200p ÷ 25 = 8p each
E   150p ÷ 15 = 10p each
8p is the lowest price per cake.

21.   E

All the answer choices are really different in this question, so you can just use estimation to quickly work out roughly how big the answer is. The mass of apples needs to be just over double the mass of sugar. So for 9 kg of sugar you'll need a bit more than 18 kg of apples. The only possible answer is 20.25 kg. Alternatively, round 9 kg to 10 kg. You need 2.25 kg of apples for every 1 kg of sugar, so for 10 kg of sugar you need roughly 10 x 2.25 = 22.5 kg. You rounded up, so you know that the answer is a bit less than 22.5 kg. Again 20.25 kg is the only possibility.

22.   14 g

20 g is two-thirds of 30 g. If there are 21 g of carbohydrate in 30 g of cereal, there will be two thirds of 21 g in 20 g of cereal.
One third of 21 g = 21 ÷ 3 = 7 g
Two thirds of 21 g = 7 x 2 = 14 g

23.   144

Each piece is $\frac{1}{3}$ m, so each metre of ribbon will make 3 pieces. There is 48 m of ribbon, so the total number of pieces = 3 x 48 . You can calculate this by partitioning 48:
(3 x 40) + (3 x 8) = 120 + 24 = 144. You could also round 48 m to 50 m and calculate 3 x 50 = 150. You added 2 m extra when rounding, so there are 3 x 2 = 6 too many pieces.
Total number of pieces = 150 – 6 = 144

24.   B

Triangle-based pyramids have 4 triangular faces, 4 vertices and 6 edges.

25.   £3919

Subtract the price Kate paid from the original price:
£6999 – £3080 = £3919. You can do this subtraction using partitioning: 6999 – 3000 – 80 = 3999 – 80 = £3919

26.   A

The horizontal line on the graph shows no distance was travelled between 09:00 and 10:30, which is 1 $\frac{1}{2}$ hours. (Read the times off the horizontal axis.) This was when they were having a break.

27.   E

403 is half of 806. So 30 x 403 must be equal to half of 30 x 806. As 30 x 806 = 24 180, 30 x 403 must be 24 180 ÷ 2 = 12 090.

28.   B

The options are all very different, so try estimating to find the answer. The base of each triangle is about 5 m, and the height of each triangle is 4 m. Area = ½ x base x height = ½ x 5 x 4 = 2.5 x 4 = 10 m². The area of each triangle is about 10 m², so the area of the patio is about 2 x 10 = 20 m². The only answer that is possible is 19.2 m².

29.   200

Work out the profit the school makes on each badge:
£1 – 70p = 30p. They made £60 or 6000p in total.
So divide 6000 by 30 to find the number of badges they bought.
6000 ÷ 30 = 200.

30.   Beef and Prawn Cocktail

According to the bar chart, 25 children said Ready Salted. Now find two other flavours for which the numbers of children add up to 25. 11 children said Beef, and 14 said Prawn Cocktail (11 + 14 = 25). This is the only pair which add to 25.

31.   22.105 litres

Add units = 5 + 5 + 5 + 5 = 20
Add tenths = 0.5 + 0.5 + 0.5 + 0.5 = 2
Add hundredths = 0.05 + 0.05 = 0.1
Add thousandths = 0.005 only
20 + 2 + 0.1 + 0.005 = 22.105 litres

32.   10

250 ÷ 12 = 20 remainder 10. 12 x 10 = 120, so 12 x 20 = 240. 250 – 240 = 10. 10 is less than 12, so no more bags can be filled. So 10 biscuits are left over.

33.   C

There are 15 sweets altogether, and 5 of them are cherry. So the chance of picking out a cherry sweet is $\frac{5}{15}$ which simplifies to $\frac{1}{3}$. (You simplify fractions by dividing the numerator and denominator by the same number — in this case 3.)

34.   194

Write down the square numbers between 46 and 91:
6 x 6 = 36 — too small, 7 x 7 = 49, 8 x 8 = 64, 9 x 9 = 81, 10 x 10 = 100 — too big. 49 + 64 + 91 = 194.

35.   14

The mode is the most common value. Tuesday and Thursday have the same number of awards. No other days have the same number. So the mode number of awards is represented by 4 full circles plus two-thirds of a circle. Each symbol is worth 3 awards, so the four full circles represent 4 x 3 = 12 awards, and the two-thirds of a circle represents 2 awards. The mode is 14 awards (12 + 2).

36.   A

Use the diagram to work out how many of each ball type there are:
Red = 4 + 7 = 11
Yellow = 6 + 3 = 9
Striped = 3 + 7 = 10
Spotted = 6 + 4 = 10
Red striped = 7.
So, out of all the options, it is most likely that a red ball (A) will be pulled out.

37.   £1.10

To calculate the mean, add up the amounts and divide by the number of months (6):
£1.20 + £0.80 + £1.50 + £1.10 + £1.50 + £0.50 = £6.60
(Remember to convert 80p to £0.80 and 50p to £0.50.)
Now divide the total by 6: £6.60 ÷ 6 = £1.10

38. 64 cm

The shape he draws is a rectangle. The rectangle is the same length as seven cubes ($7 \times 4 = 28$ cm).
The rectangle is as wide as one cube (4 cm).
So the perimeter is $28 + 28 + 4 + 4 = 64$ cm.

39. D

Count the number of small triangles in each pattern and see how they relate to the pattern number:
Pattern 1 = 1 triangle
Pattern 2 = 4 triangles
Pattern 3 = 9 triangles
Pattern 4 = 16 triangles
Pattern 5 = 25 triangles
These are all square numbers. If the pattern number is n, then the number of triangles is n^2.

40. B

The dog eats 245 g each meal, and she has $3 \times 7 = 21$ meals a week. So in one week, she eats 245 g $\times$ 21. The answers are all very different, so try estimating to find the answer. Round 245 g up to 250 g, and 21 down to 20. $250 \times 20 = 5000$ g = 5 kg. The only answer close to 5 kg is 5.145 kg.

41. £280

First work out how many hours a day the café is open for in the summer and in the winter. Mar – Sep: 9 am to 6 pm = 9 hours. Oct – Feb: 11 am to 4 pm = 5 hours. So the café is open 4 hours (9 – 5) more each day in the summer. So it's open $4 \times 7 = 28$ hours longer per week in the summer. It costs £10 per hour to run the café, so it costs $28 \times £10 = £280$ more each week in the summer.

42. 42 cm³

The net folds up to form a cuboid:

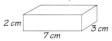

Volume = length $\times$ width $\times$ height = $7 \times 3 \times 2 = 42$ cm³

43. 1100 ml

First work out how many ml of milk Katie drinks each day: 350 ml twice a day = $350 \times 2 = 700$ ml. Now find out how much milk she drinks a week. $700 \times 7 = 4900$ ml. She starts with 6 litres of milk, which is 6000 ml. So at the end of the week, she has $6000 - 4900 = 1100$ ml left.

44. south west

There are 180° in a half turn, 90° in a right angle, and 45° in half a right angle. $225° = 180° + 45°$ = a half turn and half a right angle:

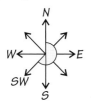

45. (2, 2)

Parallelograms have two pairs of equal parallel sides, so the completed shape will look like this:

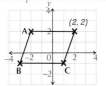

46. 8

49 is a square number — $7^2 = 49$. So if $x = 7$, $x^2 - 1 = 48$, which is less than 49, so the statement isn't true. That means the answer must be 8 — if $x = 8$, $x^2 - 1 = 63$, which is greater than 49, so the statement is true.

47. 35

Use inverses to work back from 25. To find the number divided by 7 to get 25, multiply 25 by 7: $25 \times 7 = 175$. To find the number that is multiplied by 5 to get 175, divide 175 by 5: $175 \div 5 = 35$.

48. C

Make a table of the values and their positions in the pattern:

n	1	2	3	4	5
value	–1	1	3	5	7

You might be able to spot the pattern — you double n and subtract 3 to get the value. This means the formula is $2n - 3$. If you don't spot this pattern, just substitute one of the n values into each formula in turn, and see which gives you the correct value. E.g. if $n = 2$.
A: $3n = 3 \times 2 = 6$ — not correct
B: $n - 3 = 2 - 3 = -1$ — not correct
C: $2n - 3 = 2 \times 2 - 3 = 1$ — correct
D: $2 \div n - 3 = 2 \div 2 - 3 = -2$ — not correct
E: $2n + 3 = 2 \times 2 + 3 = 7$ — not correct
Only C gives the correct value, so must be the formula.

49. £23.96

The area of the soil is $8 \times 6 = 48$ m². One tub of seed covers 12 m², so $48 \div 12 = 4$ tubs are needed. This costs $£5.99 \times 4 = £23.96$.

50. B

60% percent of an amount is $\frac{60}{100} = \frac{6}{10} = \frac{3}{5}$ of it.

If the price of an item is reduced by $\frac{3}{5}$ the new price will be $1 - \frac{3}{5} = \frac{2}{5}$ of it. So, if the amount is n, the sale price will be $\frac{2}{5}(n)$.